MW00987544

AspaClariA
Judaica
Aventura
305-937-7797

ArtScroll Series™

Rabbi Nosson Scherman / Rabbi Meir Zlotowitz

General Editors

by
**Rabbi Avrohom Katz /
Tuvia Cohen**

World

**Wonders hidden
below the surface**

Mesorah Publications, ltd

FIRST EDITION
First Impression ... November 1996
Second Impression ... August 1998
Third Impression ... October 1999
Fourth Impression ... November 2005
Fifth Impression ... February 2013

Published and Distributed by
MESORAH PUBLICATIONS, LTD.
4401 Second Avenue / Brooklyn, N.Y 11232

Distributed in Europe by
LEHMANNS
Unit E, Viking Business Park
Rolling Mill Road
Jarow, Tyne & Wear, NE32 3DP
England

Distributed in Australia and New Zealand
by **GOLDS WORLDS OF JUDAICA**
3-13 William Street
Balaclava, Melbourne 3183
Victoria, Australia

Distributed in Israel by
SIFRIATI / A. GITLER — BOOKS
6 Hayarkon Street
Bnei Brak 51127

Distributed in South Africa by
KOLLEL BOOKSHOP
Northfield Centre, 17 Northfield Avenue
Glenhazel 2192, Johannesburg, South Africa

THE ARTSCROLL SERIES™
OUR AMAZING WORLD
© *Copyright 1996, by* MESORAH PUBLICATIONS, Ltd.
4401 Second Avenue / Brooklyn, N.Y. 11232 / (718) 921-9000 / www.artscroll.com

ALL RIGHTS RESERVED
The text, prefatory and associated textual contents and introductions
— including the typographic layout, cover artwork and ornamental graphics —
have been designed, edited and revised as to content, form and style.

No part of this book may be reproduced
IN ANY FORM, PHOTOCOPYING, OR COMPUTER RETRIEVAL SYSTEMS
— even for personal use without written permission from
the copyright holder, Mesorah Publications Ltd.
except by a reviewer who wishes to quote brief passages
in connection with a review written for inclusion in magazines or newspapers.

THE RIGHTS OF THE COPYRIGHT HOLDER WILL BE STRICTLY ENFORCED.

ISBN 10: 0-89906-313-6 / ISBN 13: 978-0-89906-313-3

Typography by CompuScribe at ArtScroll Studios, Ltd.
Printed in the United States of America by Noble Book Press Corp.
Bound by Sefercraft, Quality Bookbinders, Ltd., Brooklyn N.Y. 11232

ספר זה מוקדש לזכרון עולם ולעילוי נשמות

אבי מורי

הולך תמים ופעל צדק
סמל של ישרות ועבודת ה'
בעיר ליעדז יותר מחמישים שנה

ר' אהרן ב"ר יצחק כ"ץ ז"ל
הלך לעולמו כ"ב מרחשון תשנ"ו

אמי מורתי

היקרה והדגולה, רודפת חסד ומצות
עטרת בעלה ותפארת משפחתה

מרת חיה רחל בת ר' יהושע יעקב ע"ה
הלכה לעולמה כ"ד אייר תשל"ט

RABBI B. RAKOW
RAV OF GATESHEAD
138 WHITEHALL ROAD,
GATESHEAD NE8 1TP
Tyne & Wear
TEL. 0632-773012

בצלאל כהרה"ג ר' יום טוב ליפמאן ראקאו

אב"ד דנייטסהעד

ב"ה _____ יום שלישי ל' סיון תשמ"ז

הנה יד"נ הרב שלובכם אליה הכהן קלמ שליט"א
באו לפנינו לשאול ספר צלבות הגדול ובעיקר
וראשית דבר קל' הבכה בקלאא הגדול ובכן דבר
לחתחנן ולשומע בה . האמר קל ... ... רק לשם דברם
ברום ונקיעות הקלוי יש לברלתו האשוים אל.
אותו עם עלה אקיים ... ... הבלמה והבלמם ולבמחו
דף הגדול עלצ" אל כבן אלדה שוא המקבל ה"ד
... אייבת הבדית ולבת להם
כבר ליהם מתוארכיב על נוחו לם בתב לשומ
ואתא נתקבל את ה נ... האמארנים לבכמי הלום
לבלמא לאו זה שתף
לאותו בנה לאתן ל"ד"ר ... קיבה לבין על האומי
המלמים ... לאור שלם יאה ... נגמ ונרים
יהן ן אמן

ידידו האוהבו בנוכת התורה
הק' בצלאל ראקעוו

ישיבת
בית יוסף
גייטסהעד

Gateshead Talmudical College

בס"ד

Principal
Rabbi Z. Cohen

Rosh Hayeshiva
Rabbi A. Gurwicz

88 Windermere Street, Gateshead, Tyne & Wear NE8 1UB.
Telephone: (091) 477 2616 Fax: (091) 490 0480

It is with very special joy that I write these few lines of appreciation on the unique work of a very beloved Talmid whose friendship I have cherished for over 25 years.

בעל and ירא שמים, בן תורה is renowned as a הר"ר אברהם טוביה הכהן ק"ץ שליט"א מדות. But most outstanding is his אמונה — which is what this book is all about.

The chapters of this book do not just contain clever comparisons in parable form, but they are דברים היוצאים מן הלב — sincere words emanating from a pure heart, designed to enter the heart and strengthen the reader's awareness of הקב"ה in all his surroundings.

This ספר is an updated שער הבחינה, expanding on the theme begun by the ת חובת הלבבו בעל, and continued through the years up till our times by such גדולים as the איש חזון in his קונטרס אמונה בטחון and the Steipler זצ"ל in his ספר חיי עולם.

The author of this work has his own original approach, and although his style is sometimes light, one is never diverted from the central theme of the book which is to make the reader — at the end of each chapter — gasp in astonishment and exclaim over and over again — נפלאות הבורא! נפלאות הבורא!

זכה המחבר שליט"א להיות ממזכי הרבים הגדולים בדורנו על ידי שעוריו המתוקים בכמה מוסדות בעירנו וכמה מקומות במדינתנו - ועכשיו זיכהו השי"ת להרחיב גבולו על ידי ספר נפלא זה שיגיע בעזה"י לכל קצווי תבל ותתרבה הדעת והאמונה בעולם - אשרי חלקו!

ויהי רצון שיפוצו מעייניתיו חוצה ויראה ברכה בעמלו כל הימים.

ממני הכו"ח באה"ר

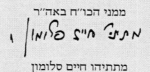

מתתיהו חיים סלומון

President: B. Guttentag esq. Hon Treasurer: I. Kaufman esq. Secretary: S. Esofsky esq.

Charity Commission No. 527414. Inland Revenue No. X57 613A.

בֵּית מֶדְרַשׁ לְמוֹרוֹת

JEWISH TEACHERS' TRAINING COLLEGE

Founded by: Mr A. KOHN

FOR TEACHERS IN DAY SCHOOLS, HEBREW CLASSES AND NURSERY - SCHOOLS

Principal: Rabbi M. MILLER

**50, BEWICK ROAD
GATESHEAD NE8 4DQ**
Telephone: 091-477 2620
091-477 1566

ב׳ה

It gives me considerable satisfaction to write a few words of approbation with regard to the book "Our Amazing World" compiled by Rabbi A. Katz who has been a most successful lecturer at the Gateshead Jewish Teachers' Training College for several years.

Rabbi Katz is endowed with an unusual gift both in the written and spoken word to demonstrate the incontrovertible wonders in the universe at large and in the personal human physique, thus accomplishing the dual function of שאו מרום עיניכם וראו מי ברא אלה — "Raise your eyes to the heavans and contemplate, 'Who created all this?'" (Yeshayah, 40:26) and מבשרי אחזה אלוק — "And from my own flesh I can perceive my Creator" (Job 19:26) in its positive sense.

Rabbi Katz's writings are infused with both wit and erudition and his style fascinates the reader. He has been a regular contributor to "Yated Ne'eman" and the present volume is a compilation of those articles.

The book is an invaluable source from which the reader will derive an appreciation of the wondrous world of the Creator and it will undoubtedly strengthen his Emunah. It is a path trodden by אברהם אבינו and commended to us by so many of our גדולים; in particular, חובות הלבבות, רמב׳׳ם and חזון איש.

In seeking to emulate their illustrious example, albeit in a modern context and idiom, Rabbi Katz has provided the reader with a wealth of material from which he can attain greater awareness of the גדלות הבורא.

I profoundly hope that "Our Amazing World" will reach the minds and hearts of a wide public to accomplish the purpose for which it was written.

Rabbi M. Miller
Principal, Gateshead J T T C

Table of Contents

cAcknowledgments

Our generation has been described as midgets standing on the shoulders of giants. In thanking those who have contributed to the production of this book, there are no shortage of giants.

First mention goes to my dear parents, *z"l*, both of whom left Germany as young refugees, and set up a home of Torah and *chesed* in the city of Leeds, England. It was they who planted and nourished the love of Judaism in their children, and it was they who gave unstinting support — financial, moral and emotional — in encouraging us to consolidate our standard of learning in Gateshead. This book is dedicated to their memory, as a small token of gratitude for the immeasurable debt that we, their children, owe them.

The Jewish community of Gateshead is modest in number, but great in quality. It is a very great privilege to live in this unique environment and to benefit from the Torah-permeated atmosphere of the town, its members, its institutions, and its leaders. Much more than mere thanks are due to the Kehillah's leader, Rabbi B. Rakow, שליט״א, for his constant, active encouragement, and to the *Roshei Yeshivah* of Gateshead Yeshivah, from whom I gained my formative education and with whom I have enjoyed a close association for more than three decades. May Hashem *Yisbarach* bless the whole Kehillah with continued peace, health, and happiness.

In common with thousands, my interest in the wisdom demonstrated by the created world was kindled by Rabbi Avigdor Miller, שליט״א, and his written word. In expressing my gratitude to him, I humbly offer a prayer that he be granted many more years, in vigor and in good health, to continue to disseminate his unique message to an ever-growing audience.

It is in the Gateshead Jewish High School for Girls that many of the chapters of this book were first delivered in oral form. My heartfelt thanks are extended to its principal, Rabbi

Dovid Bowden, for his enthusiasm and his vision in providing a forum for this very special subject to be taught. All the chapters contained in the book have appeared in article form in the weekly *Yated Ne'eman* (under the pen name Tuvia Cohen); and I am extremely grateful to the worthy editors for their permission to reprint the articles, and for their continuous friendship and encouragement.

A friend in need is a friend indeed, and no truer friend could be found than R' Dovid Morgan, who, with wisdom and adroitness, has nursed this particular project from its inception through to the finished product. Moshe Aharon Ruskin provided the photography, and his talent with the camera has contributed greatly to the finished product.

Mesorah Publications, popularly known as ArtScroll, is a publishing company who combine professionalism with pleasantness. It has been both a privilege and a pleasure to make their acquaintance, and particular thanks are due to Rabbi Nosson Scherman, the General Editor; Rabbi Avrohom Biderman, who master-minded the production; and Mrs. Judi Dick, whose skillful editing made the original Queen's English comprehensible to both sides of the Atlantic. In addition, Mrs. Faygie Weinbaum and Mrs. Tova Finkelman for their superb proofreading. and Mrs. Bassie Gutman whose pagination make my words a pleasure to look at and to read.

My dear family have no desire to be mentioned. But they deserve it, for being so loyal, encouraging and helpful. Each one is wonderful, and each one should be blessed with everything good.

The greatest thanks of all goes to Hashem *Yisbarach*, for the privilege of having been able to discover and relate a minute amount of the endless wisdom, in this, His Amazing World. May it be His will to be able to continue this work in good health, and together with all our People merit seeing the great day when all inhabitants of the world will gladly acknowledge the true Master of the Universe, the source of all wisdom.

Introduction — The Swiss Army Knife

If I were a soldier, I would join the Swiss Army. The reason for this choice is not simply the fact that Switzerland is a neutral country, and their army has not been engaged in active service for some two hundred years (although, come to think of it, that could be a major incentive) but because of the superior equipment with which their soldiers are issued.

Guns? Boots? Berets? No difference there. All armies have those. What makes the army of Switzerland the envy of the world is a diminutive piece of equipment, compact enough to slip into your pocket, but a giant of practicality. It is the famous Swiss Army knife.

Just imagine. You are a commando, behind enemy lines. Your mission — to sabotage an ammunition depot, create panic and confusion, and return safely to base. In the silence of the night, you approach the camp. Out comes the invaluable knife. With the help of the wire benders, you gain entry. Metal cutting-saw, metal file, pliers with metal-cutters and precision screwdriver make short work of the fuel tanks, and a neat hole provides evidence of the strength of your tools. You need a fuse. With the scissors blade you cut your handkerchief to the appropriate size, and stuff it in the hole. From its tiny compartment comes the match (an exclusive feature not yet available to the general public). Fire is applied to the fuse, and you run. Using the knife's integrated compass, you locate your safe hideout on a hill above the camp. In mesmerized fascination, you watch the explosions erupt. Only then, with the mission accomplished, do you realize how hungry you are. Out comes the knife again. With its can opener, you open your emergency rations. The small blade and tweezers help you retain a modicum of good manners in the most trying of conditions. Pleased that you brought your celebratory miniature bottle of wine, the corkscrew attachment is a thoughtful addition. Glancing at the ever-accurate built-in Swiss watch that graces the knife's central shaft, you note with satisfaction that the helicopter which will carry you to safety is due in five minutes. Just enough time to write your report with the knife's tiny pen, while chewing pensively on the toothpick, tastefully provided by the knife's manufacturers.

Would it ever occur to you that this knife fell into shape when the local scrap-metal merchant's yard exploded? Would you for one moment imagine that this complex tool just 'happened'? Never ever. During your return journey, you have ample opportunity to cogitate over your experiences and utter silent thanks to Charles Eisener, who in 1897 patented the first Swiss Army knife, and the nine hundred employees currently employed in the factory in Switzerland.

You don't have to be a soldier to appreciate the intelligence that this mini tool-kit demonstrates. To create twenty-nine different features in an instrument the size of a pocket penknife is a stroke of genius. You don't have to be Swiss to appreciate the ingenuity and craftsmanship demonstrated by a precision instrument that is virtually unchallenged in its versatility. And you don't have to be a biologist, botanist or zoologist to know that the world that we see around us is no less complex and ingenious.

In the created world, wherever you look, whatever you investigate, you will find wisdom. Whether it is the human liver, which weighs just three pounds but performs upwards of five hundred jobs; the owl, whose eyes have a special reflective layer behind the retina to help it see in the dark; or an individual cell, whose power stations, transport systems, manufacturing plants and communications network bear more resemblance to a large city than something that cannot even be seen without a super-microscope; the common denominator remains the same — wisdom of an incredible degree.

When the Patriarch Abraham studied the world around him, he discovered order, purpose, design and intelligence. Understanding the fundamental fact that none of these qualities produce themselves or originate from nothing, Abraham concluded that there must be a Great Intelligence responsible for them all. In the thirty-eight centuries since Abraham made his epic discovery, little has changed, other than the scope, depth and boundaries of our knowledge. If Abraham saw a world that demonstrates limitless wisdom, our generation, with the benefit of scientific research, sees it a hundred-fold. While it is true that the Jewish people have the benefit of the Torah, which substantiates Avraham's thoughts with a living tradition that the Creator identified Himself as such to His Chosen People, anyone using his mind honestly can safely arrive at the same conclusion.

There are several interesting facts that can assist the thought process. Firstly: Go to an automobile junkyard. Observe the cars in varying degrees of decay, and you learn an important fact. There is no evidence of ordering forces in nature. Quite to the contrary. There is a scientific principle called "entropy." This essentially means that there is a downward tendency from the highly organized toward the less organized. Left to themselves, things fall apart rather than organize themselves. That which applies to the junkyard, or your children's bedroom, applies to the whole world. Inanimate matter on earth simply does not search out a way to improve itself. Nor will an appeal to immense periods of time help. Time produces decay and disintegration. It results in corroding metals and eroding cliffs. Time is destructive, not constructive. Inanimate matter, devoid of energy and life to begin with, will remain inactive forever, unless acted upon by a superior outside force that can give it direction and organization. If the observable world around us is in an advanced state of order, who made it so? In the case of the Swiss Army knife, we know the name of the inventor and the manufacturer. In the case of the universe, who, or what, is that outside force?

Secondly: Scientists such as Louis Pasteur helped to show that life comes from previous life, and that spontaneous generation of new living things from non-living matter does not occur. Life — in all its myriad forms — must have had a beginning. The intelligent mind poses a question. In the world around us we see life, order and complexity. For example, think of your brain. Our knowledge of the brain is less complete than our knowledge of most other organs. This is due to the astonishingly complicated microstructure of this organ. Even if only one-hundredth of the connections in the brain were specifically organized, this would still represent a system containing a much greater number of specific connections than the entire communications network on Earth. Think of the blood circulation in your body, which is so vast that if all the blood vessels in the body's transport system were laid end to end, the total length would be in the region of 70,000 miles, or twice around the globe. In this vast transport system, there are no broken connections, and no train is ever late. Think of a single cell about as complicated as New York City. There is not a laboratory in the world that can compete with the biochemical activity of the smallest living organism. Faced with such a welter of evidence of coordination, complexity and enormous intelligence, one must make a decision. Who is responsible for it all? (It is interesting to note that the Talmud [*Bava Metzia* 25a] states that anyone finding three coins on the ground in a tower formation would have to assume that someone had placed them there purposely, and would be obliged to find the owner. The human mind would not accept that three coins could fall haphazardly one on top of the other. If there is intelligence in three coins, what about the brain?)

The choice is stark. You can arrive at an honest answer that points to a Great Intelligence. That was Avraham's conclusion, and, as stated earlier, it has since been corroborated very audibly and most powerfully by direct communication from that Great Intelligence to His Chosen People. There are, however, many who fear this logical conclusion and have mustered all their imagination to invent alternative hypotheses to explain away the evidence in front of their eyes. It is not the purpose of this book either to directly attack or destroy their theories. The reason for this is simple. Our Sages have stated that if someone has a vested interest in a certain standpoint, no amount of rational arguments will move him. After hearing Professor Harold C. Urey, Nobel Laureate in Chemistry, state, "All of us who study the origin of life find that the more we look into it, the more we feel it is too complex to have evolved anywhere . . . and yet we all believe as an article of faith that life evolved from dead matter on this planet. It is just that its complexity is so great it is hard for us to imagine that it did" (quoted in the Christian Science Monitor, January 4, 1962), you can begin to see that evolution has turned into a quasi-religion. Indeed, after hearing Dr. Francis Crick, a Cambridge University professor and Nobel Laureate for DNA research, admit that life could not have evolved on Earth, but must have been "sent here long ago in the form of germinal material from elsewhere in the universe" (quoted by A.I. Oparin in his book "Origin of Life" p. 570) then we perceive a degree of faith in the non-belief of a Creator that dwarfs anything that belief in a Creator demands! To those who believe with perfect faith in hypotheses which exclude a Creator, this is not their book.

This book addresses those who have an honest and open mind. It is designed for those who wish to follow the footsteps of Abraham. In doing so, it heeds the advice of *Rambam*, who states, "The Almighty has commanded us to love and fear Him; as it says, 'You should love Hashem your God' and 'Hashem your God you should fear.' What is the method by which one can come to love and fear Him? When one reflects on His deeds and His great and wonderful Creation, and discerns and discovers the limitless wisdom contained therein — immediately he is gripped by admiration and love for the Creator . . ." (*Hilchos Yesodei HaTorah* 2:1-2).

The Torah opens with the words, "In the beginning of God's creation . . ." which is understood by *Targum Yerushalmi* to mean "God created the world with wisdom." When our Sages looked at the world, they saw wisdom. "How great are Your works, Hashem, You make them all with wisdom" (*Morning Prayers*). "Blessed are You, our God, King of the Universe, Who fashioned man with wisdom . . ." (*Asher yatzar* blessing). This book has a simple objective: To draw attention to this vast wisdom inherent in the world that is us, and in the world around us, to help us become increasingly aware of, and admire, and hence love the Great Intelligence responsible for it all. In this respect, the motivation is similar to the earlier volume, *Designer World*. It is a humble attempt to walk in the footsteps of the Patriarch Abraham, and to emulate the great example set by so many of our eminent scholars. Its function is to make the reader think. (For that reason, the reader is strongly recommended not to read more than one chapter per sitting.) If it is successful in activating the mind of just one person, to think, ponder, and begin to gain a faint inkling of the greatness of the Creator (and even if that one person is the writer) then all the hours of effort will have been worthwhile.

It is my earnest prayer that in some small way, *Our Amazing World* will spread the recognition of, and love for the Almighty, in this, His world.

Perchance to Dream

Once upon a time, when darkness fell, people went to bed. The day's work had been done, the outside gloom was impenetrable, few ventured out at night, and all activity came to an end. If you could afford artificial light in the form of oil or candles, you could sit and learn in peace and tranquility, but if not, it was off to bed. Time has moved on, and night has become an extended day. Being city sophisticates, we are connected to the whole world by telephone, and expect everyone to be awake when we are awake. If we require a taxi at 3:30 a.m., there are 24-hour cab companies to answer our call. Do you feel famished at 2:45 in the morning, and would give anything for hot fresh bread? "No problem, sir, just run over to your local 24-hour bakery shop, and we shall be happy to oblige." If we would live in a society where the essential services (fire, ambulance and police) would shut down from 8:00 in the evening until 8:00 in the morning, we would indeed spend a very anxious 12 hours hoping that nothing would go wrong. That is the world that we live in, and we have grown accustomed to the life-style.

There are many situations in which the need to continue working through the night is absolute essential. Could you imagine boarding a plane for your night flight to *Eretz Yisrael*, knowing that after your special kosher meal has been consumed and the lights dimmed, the captain of the aircraft would join the passengers in the cabin for a restful few hours' sleep curled up in his blanket? Help! Certainly, large hotels never sleep. A typically large hotel will have up to 50 members of the staff working hard throughout the night hours. Night clerks and receptionists have to remain on duty, for guests can arrive at any time. In the kitchens, where some 3,750 meals must be prepared in the next 24 hours, the baking of bread and pastry has been under way since midnight. The overnight cleaning crew washes and scours the kitchen equipment and polishes the breakfast silverware. In the basement, the engineering team, which maintains the hotel's life-support systems — air conditioning, refrigeration, light and power, hot water — is busy keeping the hotel alive. In the housekeeping department, the last supply baskets containing changes of bed linen and towels for the guest rooms are being filled. Morning newspapers are put out for room deliveries, maintenance staff clean the public areas and arrange the rooms needed for early morning functions, such as working breakfasts and business meetings. When the hotel wakes up at 7 a.m., a tired night staff hands over the responsibilities to their daytime colleagues.

In any large and important concern, work must continue throughout the night, be it an airport, large department

Sleep well, little one. While you sleep wonders are taking place within you.

store, electricity generating plant, railroad station, ocean liner, or YOU.

"Did you say me? To the best of my knowledge I am neither a train, nor an airport, neither a hotel nor an ocean liner!" That is true, you are neither one nor the other — you are in fact far more complex than the sum total of them all; and work must continue day and night.

Everyone needs to sleep. How do you fall asleep? It is possible that you have trained yourself to sleep at a specific time. Your 'biological clock' tells you that you are tired, you give a big yawn (this is an involuntary reflex action in which you open your mouth wide and release breath slowly; although it may also be a sign of insufficient fresh air, boredom, or even just seeing someone else yawn!) and prepare for sleep. Sleep can also be caused by sheer lack of sleep, by immobility, monotony, warmth, or just simply lack of purpose. (Next time you fall asleep in a *shiur*, ask yourself which of the above was the cause!) As sleep slowly creeps in, the heart slows, blood pressure falls, the muscles relax (sometimes you know that you are about to fall asleep when you feel a muscular spasm — portrayed in your dreamy half-sleep as a feeling of falling over), the pupils of the eyes become smaller, and the electronical brain waves change in appearance. You flit to and fro from wakefulness to drowsiness, and lose control of your thoughts. You are slow to react to stimuli, and you might find yourself talking rubbish. If you are driving in this condition — Stop!

Like furrows on the ocean floor, so there are different levels of sleep. The first level is a kind of twilight between wakefulness and sleep. Another level is where, underneath the closed eyelids, there is rapid eye movement, and much body movement. Then there is 'deep sleep' where the muscles are completely relaxed, there is no eye movement, and the sleeper is oblivious to sound, and can only be awakened with difficulty. If you are going to sleepwalk, it will be during this type of sleep! This stage of sleep is the deep, restorative quiet sleep associated with 'a good night's rest.' The common denominator of all types of sleep is a loss of consciousness. Since your mind is not in control (as indicated by sleeptalking, sleepwalking, teeth-grinding, snoring . . .) and you are not in a conscious position to issue orders, how are the vital services in your body notified that they must continue? Listen and be amazed!

There are two types of muscular action. One is voluntary, like the movement of your eyes, legs and hands; the other is involuntary, like the movement of food down your food-pipe, or the beating of your heart. Some muscles are both voluntary and involuntary. You can increase the times that you blink your eyes, but you cannot prevent your eyes from blinking. You can take a deep breath on the instructions of

you doctor, but you cannot tell yourself to stop breathing . . .
for too long! It is this involuntary capability of the muscles
to which we owe our lives while asleep. Imagine that when
you 'switched off' by falling asleep, your brain also decided to
have an eight-hour break! Heaven forbid! So while the hotel
sleeps, the vital services carry on faithfully, conscientiously
and efficiently. Imagine that you had a sumptuous Friday
night meal, going overboard with regard to all the various
dishes. Feeling very satisfied and more than full, you decided
to go to bed. What work you have given your stomach!
However, when you wake up in time for Shabbos *Shacharis*
(Sabbath morning prayers), everything will be in perfect order. The stomach department, in conjunction with the
kidneys, liver and intestines, not to mention the blood supply
and nervous system, will have quietly and dutifully processed
all the ingredients of the banquet. The pantry will have been
emptied, and all the protein, fat and carbohydrates will have
been sent to their correct destination; the waste material will
have been carefully sorted, ready for evacuation. You don't
have to give them any instruction, they know better than
you what to do. Who told them — who programmed the wonderful machine!? What thanks one owes the Creator when
one wakes up and everything is in order!*

Think a little more. While you sleep, you have dreams. In
your dreams, you walk, run, jump — in a dream everything is
possible. But all the time, you lie perfectly still! It appears
that there is a cut-off mechanism in the brain which sus-
pends physical activity, even though the same brain is
thinking thoughts of those actions. Imagine what havoc
would be wreaked if every dream was acted out!

In our hotel, important maintenance work is carried out
at night. The body is the most wonderful hotel you could
think of. The brain cells renew themselves, not by cell divi-
sion as in the rest of the body, but by replacing the protein
molecules ('turnover'). The greatest rate of brain protein synthesis takes place during sleep. Similarly, the greatest rate of

---

* See further, Just Leave It to Us.

cell replacement in the skin, production of red blood cells, and secretion of growth hormone all take place during the restful hours of sleep. Is it any wonder that sleep is considered, and instinctively felt, to be a cure? Very often, facts, words, or ideas that were only vaguely understood the night before are crystal clear and organized when you wake up. Since the brain protein has had a chance to renew itself, and memory traces are strengthened during sleep, this can be well understood. Delaying the making of a decision in the evening and waiting until 'one sleeps on it' is more than just a saying — it is the best of sense based on the design of sleep. While you sleep, your brain is renewing itself, and data is reshuffled in such a way as to provide a fresh perspective to problems that seemed intractable. When is the very best time in the day to learn? In the morning when your brain is at its freshest. What service!

You think it is something special when you put your shoes outside the door (in a hotel, not your home!) and the next morning they are shiny and clean. Think of the service your very own body provides every night. Never mind your shoes, it is you yourself that has been refreshed, renewed, a little taller, clearer in mind, all food processed and dirty dishes washed, ready and eager to begin a new day. And all absolutely free. All we have to do is think a little — and thank a lot.

מוֹדֶה אֲנִי לְפָנֶיךָ מֶלֶךְ חַי וְקַיָּם שֶׁהֶחֱזַרְתָּ בִּי נִשְׁמָתִי . . .

*I gratefully thank You, O living and eternal King,
for You have returned my soul within me . . .*

The Skyscraper

There is nothing like enthusiasm. If you have it, anything is possible; if you don't, everything is difficult. There once was a man who had moved to a new house with his family. Succos was approaching, and he was enthusiastic. He wanted to build his own *succah*. The fact that he had never before built a *succah*, and practical building knowledge was not one of his strong points, in no way discouraged him. With enthusiasm, he set about his task. Hardboard walls were attached to the brick wall of the house with an assortment of adhesives, bent masonry nails, screws (banged in with a

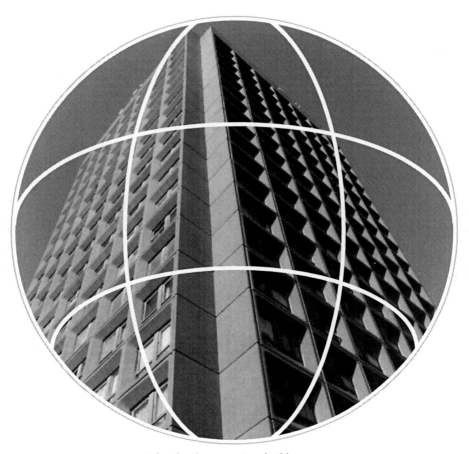

What the skyscraper is to buildings . . .

hammer) and wishful thinking. The frail structure was topped with sturdy beams on which the *schach* (*succah* roof) was to lie. A little reflection, or practical knowledge, would have suggested that the beams were far to heavy for such thin walls — but when enthusiasm is at work, practical advice is not welcome!

When Succos arrived, the builder looked at the finished product with undiluted pride, while everyone else looked at it with undisguised nervousness. On the first day, they had as their special guest an elderly lady for whom eating a meal in the *succah* (as opposed to just *Kiddush* and a piece of cake) was something of a novelty. Everything was fine until the

. . . the giraffe is to animals, only much more graceful, and much more intricate.

chicken soup was served. It was at that moment, with a re-sounding crash, that one of the sturdy beams holding up the *schach* decided to part company with the hardboard wall and instead joined the noodles in the chicken soup. Unfortunately for the lady, the plate the beam chose was hers. Shocked to the core, besplattered with the contents of her plate, the poor lady weakly asked if she could complete her meal indoors. The master builder was profusely apologetic, not compre-hending how such a catastrophe could have occurred. Never again was his enthusiasm allowed to venture to *succah* con-struction, and never again did the elderly lady accept a Succos invitation!

Enthusiasm is fine, but is no substitute for knowledge. Even the seemingly simple task of building a brick wall requires technical know-how. Without proper foundations, a plumb line and level, and one brick placed covering the joint of the two below, your wall will not last too long. Can you imagine what planning, detailed design and technical wisdom are involved in building a skyscraper! How, for example, does the water in the taps reach the 100th floor of the soaring Twin Towers? No water pressure in the mains down below would suffice to send the water to such a height. (Ten floors, or a height of 100 feet, is the most that water can reach.) Design to the rescue, please! Special pumps are installed throughout the building to speed the water on its way. A skyscraper built with lots of enthusiasm and little design would last as long as a tower built with a pack of cards.

There is an animal that lives in the wild that towers above all others. It chews the cud, has split hooves, and is everybody's favorite in the zoo. It is the skyscraper of the animal world. Enter the giraffe! As it ambles in with its distinctive gait (it moves both legs on one side of its body forward, and then both legs on the other side) you will be overawed by its colossal size. Everything about it is awesome! You will be pleased to know that a male giraffe stands about 12 feet at its shoulder (a man can easily stand between its front legs) and then towers to 19 feet at its head (some even taller). Even its baby is five feet tall at birth, is able to stand on its long thin legs after half an hour, and at the ripe old age of two hours is already capable of prancing around. In the same way that every aspect of the real skyscraper (man-made) demonstrates design, let us examine some of the many features of the animal version, which likewise demonstrate the most cunning design.

The giraffe, with its enormous brown eyes and herbivorous diet, seems a gentle animal. Indeed it is not a malicious creature, but one must be very careful indeed of frightening or exciting it, for it is prone to panic, and the results can be devastating. Its only enemy in the animal world is the lion, but the giraffe is well equipped to deal with any potential threat. If any predator, man or lion, is foolish enough to come within striking distance of its mighty hoofs, it might not live to regret it. The giraffe's hoof is 12 inches wide, and, swinging on a seven or eight-foot shaft of heavy bone and muscle and backed by terrific driving power, it can inflict a blow which has been known to knock the head off a lioness. Not only that, the hoof can kick with equal force in all four directions. If you consider that a man can only kick with full force in a forward direction (think of football), and kicking sideways produces only a weak imitation, then you understand that the giraffe's hip joint has a different construction than our own, specifically designed for the requirements and the survival of its owner.

Sending water to the top of the skyscraper requires a specially located pump. The giraffe is no different. The great height of its head demands a very high blood pressure to drive the blood up to the top. Its special pump, the heart, is able to produce that pressure. On the other hand, when the animal drinks, its head is suddenly lowered seven feet below the level of the heart. A few seconds later it might be lifted nearly 20 feet into the air! The implications of this phenonemon are potentially devastating. What should happen when the head is suddenly lowered is that the poor animal should be stricken with a brain hemorrhage (especially bearing in mind the strong blood pressure), the result of a huge rush of blood to its head. Conversely, the rapid raising of its head should drain all the blood from its head, causing immediate unconsciousness. The fact that neither happens is the result of a specially designed valve which instantly and effectively controls the blood supply, to prevent the dramatic fluxes in pressure from felling its owner. Humans do not possess this special valve — they have no need for it. The giraffe could not survive without it, and so it is an integral and vital part of its equipment. (The rhetorical question — Which came first, the long neck or the special valve — is especially appropriate here. A long neck has no purpose. The logical conclusion? They must have both been present from the time of Creation.)

Have you ever seen hair growing from lips? The giraffe's lips are long, capable of grasping, and quite hairy, a protection against the stabbing thorns of its favorite food, the leaves of the acacia tree. Its tongue is approximately 18 inches long and curls around the leaves of the acacia (thorns and all) with complete immunity to pain, and the giraffe swallows this prickly fodder without the slightest discomfort. The most impressive feature of a giraffe is, of course, its long neck, which interestingly enough is made up of seven vertebrae, exactly the same number as all other mammals. It's just that those seven vertebrae are extremely elongated! The giraffe, as well as having split hoofs, also chews the cud. What happens is that the stomach ejects a ball of food upwards, which is actually visible as it travels up the neck to the mouth. It is then chewed about 40 times, and then swallowed again. This capability is no less a feature of design than the valve in its heart. Our feeding habits do not require re-chewing semi-digested food, and so we cannot signal our stomachs to send up mouthfuls of cud, whereas the giraffe, in keeping with all kosher animals, requires this function, and is designed with the capability to perform it.

Imagine that you are in a dusty room, Pesach cleaning. All the dust flying around makes you choke and sneeze. Why don't you close your nostrils? Go on, try it! No, not with your hands — just use your nostril muscles. You can't? What a shame! Our friendly giraffe can close its nostrils completely to keep out sand and dust, just one of the many features which enable it to survive.

Another feature is its color. The giraffe is not a small animal, and any creature 20 feet tall is bound to feel just a little conspicuous. If that would only have social consequences, it would not be so bad, but if it means that you are easily visible to hungry lions (and if the lion jumps on the giraffe's back, the lion has won!) it is a serious danger. For that reason, giraffes have been provided with patchlike markings ranging from light brownish-yellow to dark brown. The lines that separate the patches are lighter in color. This color pattern (interestingly enough, each and every giraffe has a distinct coat pattern) helps to protect them by making them hard to see when they stand among trees. Like thousands of animals, camouflage is their lifesaver. Would you say that a foreign spy dressed with the greatest care to blend into the local population is an accident? Can you think of anything that demonstrates greater planning?

Take a long look at a giraffe, the graceful inoffensive giant of animals. What the skyscraper is to buildings, the giraffe is to animals, with its intricate plumbing, pumping system, defenses, its feeding and its camouflage. Whether building Succos, skyscrapers, or looking at giraffes — it is good to be knowledgeable, and then enthusiastic!

מַה גָּדְלוּ מַעֲשֶׂיךָ ה' מְאֹד עָמְקוּ מַחְשְׁבֹתֶיךָ.

אִישׁ בַּעַר לֹא יֵדָע - וּכְסִיל לֹא יָבִין אֶת זֹאת . . .

How great are Your deeds, Hashem;
exceedingly profound are Your thoughts.
A boor cannot know,
nor can a fool understand this . . .

Designed to Please

One of the most interesting things about people is that they are so different. As well as the great diversity in appearance, there is the equivalent dissimilarity in character. One of the most important lessons to be learned in the art of getting along with everyone is the necessity to accept that each person has his own distinct personality, and rightly so.

There is one area of life, perhaps not a vital area, but of interest nevertheless, where difference of character is very pronounced. That is the varied approach which different groups of people demonstrate in the presentation of food. Let us consider two extremes. On one hand you might find a young gentleman who has spent some time at summer camp, where campers like their counselors, were more concerned with functionality than amenities. In the rough and tumble of that noble establishment, the predominant word is pragmatic, not a great emphasis is laid on teaspoons, which are often not available. Now it might happen that the camp decides to serve yogurt, which you are entitled to think requires the use of a teaspoon. That is where invention born from necessity finds its natural place. Any implement, ranging from a fork, knife, or soup spoon, will suffice. Do you need to stir your coffee? That does not present a problem — take a second cup and simply pour repeatedly from one to the other, or even more simply, use your pen! In this environment it's perfectly normal to use a bent wire clotheshanger as a hatstand, two bricks as the fourth leg of a bed, and a happy make-do approach to the formalities of dining-room etiquette. It would not be considered unusual to eat canned fruit out of the can, or to happily demolish a fresh *challah* by tearing off chunks, but it would be an unusual sight to see a camper standing in the corner of the dining room obviously frantic because there was no fork laid at his place!

In stark contrast, there are those who are most particular about the manner in which food is presented. Usually of the opposite gender to the aforementioned, even the thought of eating breakfast at a table without a tablecloth, napkin (Irish linen with a napkin holder matching the china), and silver-plated bread basket would be horrific. To such people, the setting of a table is an art, and only one standard is permitted — perfection. To attend a *simchah* arranged by such an individual is a feast. Not only can you expect the meal to be something exquisite (no lukewarm oil-saturated semi-roasted potatoes and sad chicken at this affair) but it will be a delight to the eye. Naturally, the napkins and tablecloth, ribbon running down the middle of the table and *bencher* covers will all be one blended color-scheme. The fortunate guest will be dazzled with a splendid assortment of glasses, silverware (no problem here of not having a fork, the problem will be which of the six to use!) and delicate plates, the dainty dishes will have paper umbrellas protecting them (how people ever managed to make *sheva brachos* without little paper umbrellas poking out of the first course remains one of life's great mysteries), and the floral and fruit arrangements gracing the center of the table will be nothing short of spectacular.

There is no doubt whatsoever which of the two extremes people prefer. In fact, if the two extremes marry, the former is usually very happy to conform to the niceties of civilization, whereas the latter will never ever stir her coffee with her pen. If the pleasing presentation of food in the dining room is indicative of thought and consideration towards the feelings of the consumer, what would you say to the beautiful appearance of fruit and vegetables?

It is said that the best things in life are free. If so, it follows that even if you have to pay for something, the cheaper it is, the better it will be. What is cheaper than an onion? For a few pennies, you can be the proud owner of a bag of large, nutritious onions. Take a look at an onion, as if you had never seen one before. Symmetrical in proportion, round and firm in shape, and noble in appearance, it positively invites you to partake of its goodness. See how conveniently packaged it is, with the paper-thin wrapper ready to peel off effortlessly. Eat onions raw for their pungent taste, fry them for their delicious aroma, cook them for their distinctive flavor, or pickle them for posterity. Strong-tasting onions add character to what otherwise would be bland and featureless meat and soup; whereas the mild variety can be eaten raw in salads or sandwiches. Onions in your diet will stimulate the flow of digestive juices, and help in digestion. Onion juice will kill bacteria, help to lower blood pressure, and can be used to heal wounds. While under its protective wrapper, an onion has no aroma whatsoever (most considerate); it is only when it removes its coat that it informs you of its presence. No self-respecting kitchen would be without onions, and no one would begin her *Shabbos* cooking (whether for the fish, meat, or *cholent* and, naturally, the eggs with onion) without first

Eat onions raw for their pungent taste, fry them for their delicious aroma, cook them for their distinctive flavor . . .

purchasing a plentiful supply of this precious gift from the Master Creator.

Do you feel thirsty? Well, you have a choice. You could open a bottle of 'refreshing, exhilarating, real-fruit-flavored Zing,' the completely natural beverage (complete with artificial flavoring, artificial sweetener, artificial coloring, preservatives and assorted chemicals — in short, paint!). Alternatively, you could spend a fraction of the amount, and open an orange. You only have to look at an orange to understand the message that it is shouting to you. Notice me! Brightly colored and round, it is no wonder that if you were to draw two little eyes with a broad semicircular line beneath them onto the orange, you would behold the broadest, cheeriest grin ever seen on rosy cheeks. The interior of the orange is soft and vulnerable, therefore you should admire how the fruit has been provided with a tough leathery peel. Remove the orange peel, and toss it into the garbage. Not so fast! Take a look. The peel consists of the distinctly colored outer layer (called the flavedo), and the white, spongy inner layer (eaten by some people, and called the albedo). The flavedo contains tiny glands that produce a strong spicy oil, much loved by young boys to squirt at their older brothers.

Now that the orange is open, examine the interior. There are between 10 and 15 segments — each mysteriously attached to its neighbor, but capable of being detached without effort — each containing hundreds of individual juice sacs. It is not surprising that the fruit is so refreshing, containing as it does a drink that is full of sugars, which endow it with its sweetness, and at the same time blended with acids, to quench one's thirst. In case you thought that was insufficient value for money, the humble little orange is rich in vitamin C. This vitamin (which the body does not produce itself, and therefore must obtain from dietary sources) helps to heal wounds, burns and bleeding gums. It helps in decreasing blood cholesterol, acts as a natural laxative, aids in the treatment of and prevention of the common cold, lowers the incidence of blood clots in the veins, and prevents the disease of scurvy. You will also find vitamin C in other citrus fruits, green and leafy vegetables, tomatoes, cauliflower and potatoes. This vital substance (without which so many early sailors, existing on diets lacking fresh fruit and vegetables on their long voyages, contracted scurvy and never reached their destination) is manufactured using the raw materials of soil, a dash of rain and a flash of sunshine. How? Ask the Designer!

In any competition for the presentation of appetizing food, could anything beat a small fruit that is greatly valued, delicious to the palate, and the favorite of jam-manufacturers — the ever popular strawberry. Take a strawberry in your hand, and before you eat it, appreciate what you are holding!

Its aroma has no equal, its taste is sweet and nourishing, and, like so many fruits, it is color-coded to inform you of the precise moment when it is at its optimum state of ripeness. Is it surprising that it is so popular? Look at its color — red, cheerful, bright and radiant. Its surface is embedded with tiny seeds, some of which will survive the perilous journey through the digestive system to implant themselves on some fertile patch of ground, and further propagate the species. The fruit is designed with a leafy crown from which radiate small leaf clusters which, if allowed to remain on the fruit, would take root and grow new plants. The most beautiful of fruits, aromatic and nutritious, comes complete with the machinery that will guarantee the ability of future generations to partake of its goodness. Some presentation!

Look at the fruit bowl, with its raspberries, blueberries and blackberries; grapefruit, lime and tangerine; ugli, kumquat and clementine; dessert grapes, wine grapes and dried grapes; passion fruit, guava and sapodilla; cherries, plums and pears; peaches, nectarines and apricots . . . the list goes on and on, with each fruit and vegetable possessing its own unique taste, aroma and charm.

What a presentation, what concern for detail and thought to please, what wisdom each one contains, and what kindness from the One Who provided them all for our benefit and enjoyment.

בָּרוּךְ אַתָּה ה' . . . בּוֹרֵא פְּרִי הָעֵץ . . . בּוֹרֵא פְּרִי הָאֲדָמָה.
Blessed are You, Hashem,
. . . Who creates the fruit of the tree.
. . . Who creates the fruit of the ground.

Liquid Gold

Have you ever heard of Rumpelstiltskin? He is the hero, or rather the villain, of a tale told in many countries of a certain miller, poor of pocket but rich in imagination. He was blessed with a clever daughter and was immensely proud of her, to the extent that he rather foolishly boasted to the king of the land that his daughter had the ability to spin straw into gold. This sounded like an interesting proposition to the king, and he ordered the girl to be brought before him. He led her into a room where there was a great quantity of straw, presented her with a spinning wheel, and invited her to spin the straw into gold before morning. Not being too subtle, he bluntly warned her that if she failed to produce the goods, her life would have little value. Poor girl — all her protestations that the task was impossible were in vain, the door was locked, and she remained all alone with her straw.

It was then that Rumpelstiltskin turned up, noticed her weeping and sobbing, and asked if he could be of assistance. She informed the little man of the impossible task facing her, and the consequences of failure. Being a particularly capable and helpful individual, he offered to complete the contract for her, in return for an item of jewelry. The astonished girl immediately agreed, and by morning the room was full of spun gold. The story continues with the king — a prime example of one who loves gold never having enough — becoming desirous of ever greater quantities of that material, making more demands of the hapless girl, who in turn becomes increasingly dependent on the none-too-pleasant Rumpelstiltskin for assistance. As in all stories of make-believe, the girl eventually marries the king (presumably his *mechutan*, the miller, retires on the strength of his newly found social status), and Rumpelstiltskin stamps his foot on the ground in a rage with unfortunate consequences. He is the only one in the gripping tale who did not live happily ever after!

The story might appear inconsequential — it is, after all, a fairy tale; but the problem faced by the young girl is all too real. You have to imagine that you are faced with her problem. A pile of straw confronts you, and you have until morning to transform the uninspiring stack into gleaming gold. Your very life and the lives of your loved ones depend on the success of your efforts. Fail, and the consequences will be fatal. Succeed, and you will live. There is no Rumpelstiltskin who will appear out of the blue, nor are there any magic genies who will pop out of jars. This is the cold world of reality, and the problem is very real. Do you believe it?

Nothing could be more true. Consider: A cow stands in the field. Before it stretches a field covered with delicious green grass. A feast for a cow! This cow has just given birth to a fine little calf, which is healthy, sturdy, and very hungry. Within 12 hours, the little calf will require approximately six liters of highly specialized liquid, called milk. This first milk is no ordinary milk. Forget about your formula substitutes — the newly born calf needs its mother's first milk in order to survive. The first milk is called colostrum, and colostrum contains not only food, but maternal antibodies that will protect the young calf against all the common infections it is likely to encounter in its early life. It is an amazing fact that the structure of the calf's intestine will only allow the passage of the large protein antibodies from its mother in the first half-day of its life. By the time the calf reaches the grand old age of 16 hours, the intestine's capacity to absorb whole antibodies has practically ceased. Time is therefore vital — that colostrum (first milk) with its life-saving properties must be on tap in large quantities by morning at the latest!

And the only raw material that the cow can utilize is green grass. Is the task of the cow any different from that of the miller's daughter? It is indeed very different. For gold is one metal, containing one substance. Milk is comparable to a full pantry. It contains solids, water and fat. The solids include nitrogen, which in turn contain protein (albumin, globulin and casein), vitamins and minerals, plus lactose. The fat contains triglycerides, together with fat-soluble carotenes, vitamins and phospholipids. Fairy tales can conjure up fictitious old Rumpelstiltskins, but who is going to help the cow?! The life of her little one depends on her — just as the mother depended on her own mother before her — and everyone produces the goods. How on earth do they do it?

The cow has been blessed with an udder. Far from being just 'a milk bag,' the udder is in fact a remarkable factory capable of the most breathtaking feats. Construction of this factory begins when the cow is but three months old; while it is expecting its first calf special hormones speed up the process, and by the time the baby is born, the factory is ready to begin production. Each udder is in fact composed of four quarters, with 60% of the milk being produced by the hind

Liquid Gold — delivered daily to your doorstep!

quarters. The udder contains special cells (*alveolar* cells) which are the master chemists that actually synthesize and secrete the various ingredients that constitute milk. The liquid is then discharged into ducts, sinuses and cisterns, ready for collection.

From what is this milk made? A large amount of blood flows through the udder (approximately 500 liters of blood for each liter of milk produced) and some milk constituents transfer directly from blood to milk. The milk fat is made up of fatty acids derived both from synthesis in the udder and by transfer from the blood. The lactose in milk (milk sugar) is derived mainly from blood glucose, and the milk protein is derived mainly from the amino acids present in the blood. Other items taken from the blood are calcium, phosphorus, and magnesium, in addition to potassium, sodium, chlorine and vitamins A and B complex, C, D, E and K! To say that the cow simply (simply!) transforms grass into milk is a massive understatement. The cow is a chemical factory, taking all the necessary ingredients from the grass, digesting them, changing them magically into blood, and then changing all the ingredients necessary for the most complete food on earth from raw red blood to pure white milk. And the cow just munches its grass contentedly, absolutely unaware of the wonders and complexities taking place within. Move over, fairy tales — retire, old Rumpelstiltskin; the miraculous designs of everyday life, on which life depends, are far superior to anything that fiction can dream up.

If the cow is inspiring, then we human beings are even more so. The milk that the human mother produces is the most complete food in existence (not unlike the manna), ideally suited to the needs of the baby. It supplies the growing infant with all its requirements, in ideal proportions. No formula yet invented can make the claim that it meets this exacting criterion. Cow's milk is ideally suited to calves (the enzymes present in cow's milk are ideal for the calf's multistomach digestive system), but humans do not have several stomachs. Specific proteins in milk are capable of destroying harmful bacteria or protecting the young against infection that may enter the blood stream. Those in cow's milk furnish protection against diseases in the cow, whereas mother's milk protects her baby against the threats from his own environment. Mother's milk is a unique and unmatched commodity, and it can never be duplicated. Milk is the perfect food for the young infant, and its composition varies with the age of the baby, becoming gradually more concentrated. At the same time, the baby's digestion improves.

Where will you find a liquid which can compare? The first milk of the mother is also called colostrum, is low in fat and carbohydrates, and high in protein. It is exceptionally easy to digest, and is a superb 'pick-me-up' for the newborn. It is loaded with living cells that rush to the newborn baby's defense against a number of potentially harmful agents. It is alive with protective white cells (leucocytes), which are also found in blood, and are the body's chief defense against infections. What is absolutely astounding is that the mother can deliver a particular antibody in response to a new threat to the baby. Even when the needed immune agent has not been present in the mother's blood, a chain of events begins when the baby is beset by a new germ. He, of course, continues to feed from his mother, and the offending organism is passed from baby to mother. In ways not yet fully understood, the mother produces a matching immunoglobulin (immune agent) on site, locally, and sends the protective element along to the baby in the milk! It is a system of specialized programming, with the nursing mother making on demand antibodies to germs that challenge her baby. Baby places the order, and mother obligingly programs the cells and delivers the appropriate antibody in the morning's milk — and neither mother nor baby have the faintest inkling what wonders are taking place within them!

Is there any food like it? Milk is the superior food, with every species producing a tailor-made meal of perfection for its young, giving it all the nutrition and protection that it requires. Yet it is all produced from the most basic ingredients, from grass to boiled potatoes, in a manner which man, with all his wisdom, can never hope to duplicate. Produced by a Creator Whose wisdom is limitless, this life-giving liquid is indeed more precious than gold. We can only stand in awe and offer our humble thanks.

Material Benefits

Everyone dreams of being stranded on a desert island. To some it is a pleasant dream, with visions of favorite musical tapes wafting their mellifluous tones through the warm fragrant air, with golden pristine sand touching the azure blue sea in a murmur of contentment. Palm trees nod their coconut-laden branches in the soft breeze, and idyllic serenity encompasses the island. To others it is a horrifying nightmare. Thoughts of utter loneliness fill one with dread, with the frightening possibility of hostile eyes watching his every move through an undergrowth crawling with every species of insect and reptile known to mankind as an ever present possibility. How would he eat? He has never been a farmer, and the chances of finding a branch of his local friendly delicatessen are remote. Alone, vulnerable, defenseless, frightened, starving — with no Swiss Family Robinson or Robinson Crusoe to rush to his assistance — he is filled with appalling terror. It is likely that the second scenario is more representative of reality than the first figment of imagination.

Think about clothing. The dark-blue suit and smart black hat (brim up or down according to your taste) that your apparel consisted of when you were shipwrecked, has now finally worn out; what would you wear? Remember that you never joined the Boy Scouts, so that the skill of sewing together leaves to provide shirt, socks, tie and jacket are not part of your repertoire — how then will you manage? You can construct a semblance of a hut out of branches and driftwood, but it is a little difficult to fashion a sweater out of logs! You can eat wild strawberries, and you can drink water from a mountain spring, but you can't wear them — what would you do? How about growing your own clothing? Tell your body to grow its own clothes; after all, this is an emergency! Perhaps you should plant your own clothes — place a button into the sandy soil and tend it carefully with water, speak kindly to it and encourage it to grow into a full-sized overcoat. Why not? Can you suggest an alternative? Maybe you could go to one of the little insects which abound in your claustrophobic hut and ask it if it would be so kind as to spin you some clothes to wear, and in return you will faithfully feed it all the leaves it can consume. Nu, why not, you have to be practical!

Imagine, therefore, what life would be like without the material to fashion clothes; and an appreciation for the raw materials that exit all around us begins to develop. After a little investigation, it will become clear that what we considered a laughable impossibility — clothes growing from bodies, garments growing from the ground, and textiles produced by tiny insects — is in fact what happens.

There is no animal in the world less exciting than a sheep. Sheep are so boring that just counting them is a guaranteed cure for insomnia. They munch grass, say Baa-aa, and follow each other like . . .! Until you begin to think. Why is it that they can survive the harshest of winters, why do they not become soggy in the rain, why do they need such minimal care? The answer is that mankind has been provided with an animal that grows its own clothing, can live virtually anywhere, and is content to feed itself on a never-changing diet of grass and water. Most important of all, it is a docile, harmless creature that is only too happy if someone comes along with a pair of shears and removes its coat. Just imagine if the wonder-product wool would grow on the back of a lion or crocodile — we would not be wearing much wool!

There is nothing quite like wool, and there are more than 900 million sheep throughout the world to nod their assent. (There are actually more sheep in Australia than people, 133 million to be precise.) Wool is tailor-made for use by humans as clothing. It is soft and springy and the woven fibers create millions of tiny pockets of air which trap the heat inside. The secret of birds' and ducks' ability to remain warm in freezing air and water, namely, trapping a layer of warm air beneath their feathers, is a secret shared by the sheep. Wool is able to breathe, something that no man-made fiber can do. When we get hot, our bodies give out moisture. The fibers of wool can absorb this moisture, which then evaporates into the air, keeping our bodies warm and dry. If you look at a single fiber of wool under a microscope, you will see that the fiber is covered in scales, each one overlapping the other. This effectively repels water, and is the reason why wool is slightly waterproof. Wool is naturally safe — it will resist intense heat and even flames, and the moisture which it contains prevents static electricity from building up. (If you work on a powerline, make sure that you wear woolen clothing!)

Every single fiber of wool grows from its own root in the skin, called a follicle. Every follicle is an individual factory, producing cylindrical structures made of the protein, keratin. Every follicle is attached to a nerve (which registers

If you are going to be stranded on a desert island, don't forget your sheep!

pain when you pull a single hair), and to a muscle which enables it to stand on end when frightened! Your typical merino sheep has been endowed with about 100 million such factories (someone has counted them!), each one a loud and clear demonstration of design. In addition to its other qualities, wool is naturally wavy, and this gives the fiber natural elasticity. The fibers can be twisted and stretched a long way, but they will always spring back into their original position. For this reason wool is easy to dye, and difficult to burn. It stays cleaner longer than other fabrics and is extremely durable. If you do become stranded on a desert island, make sure that you take your little lamb with you, and your wardrobe is assured. This particular wardrobe has the additional advantage that it can be eaten — an edible clothing factory! Without this humble animal, clothing would be an enormous problem; with it, life is wonderful, comfortable and tasty. It surely is no accident.

Plant your clothes? No problem if the material you need is cotton. Half the fibers used by the world's textile industry are cotton. Nothing could be simpler than growing cotton, and little is more amazing. Take some warm soil, good and moist, and plant a little cotton seed. Just five days later, the seedling will appear above ground. Five or six weeks later, the first flower buds appear. Wait another three weeks, and these buds will have become flowers. The flowers only last three days, after which they fall off, leaving behind a small pod. This little pod is called the boll (rhymes with 'coal') and it contains about 30 seeds. At the same time that the flower opens, fibers of cotton (containing mainly cellulose, with a small amount of mineral salts and wax) begin to grow from each seed. A typical boll can contain up to 500,000 fibers of cotton. Each fiber grows to its full length in three weeks, and in the following weeks each fiber gets thicker as layers of cellulose build up the cell walls. Suddenly, when it can no longer take the pressure, the boll splits open, and the raw cotton fibers burst out to dry in the sun.

There you have a field of cotton bolls, like blobs of fresh snow, waiting to be harvested. Then comes ginning, baling, spinning, warping, wefting, weaving, knitting, dyeing, printing and finishing until finally you have a fabric which is strong (it is the cellulose that enables cotton to absorb large amounts of water) and comfortable. Its ability to absorb water so well makes cotton easy to wash, and is why it is the ideal material to wear near the skin and to use for bandages and towels. In addition to producing clothes, this humble little plant gives nourishment. Cotton seed contains oil, which is edible, and can be converted into margarine. The kernels can then be ground into 'meal,' rich in protein and much loved by cattle. If you have no cattle, use it for fertilizer. And if all else fails, use the cotton cellulose to manufacture paper money and a passport. If you are going to be stranded on your deserted island, try to organize some cotton plants, and you will have clothing, bedding, food for you and your animals — and even passport and money to enable you to buy your ticket home! All that from one humble plant. Who can now take cotton for granted!

Which little insect should provide us with the most treasured material for clothing? The diminutive silkworm. This tiny creature hatches from an egg, and begins to feed on mulberry leaves for over a month. During that time, it increases its body weight 10,000 times! Even breathing does not interfere with its eating, because it breathes through holes in its body. After this substantial meal, the worm sets about making its cocoon, which effectively will be its home while it turns into a moth. To make its cocoon, it exudes a semiliquid mixture from the two silk glands that run the length of its body. The single thread which emerges is made up of the two threads joined together. By tossing its head in a figure-eight motion, it slowly builds up a waterproof cocoon that completely surrounds it. It takes a worm about three days to spin the entire cocoon, during which it will have shaken its head an amazing 300,00 times! A perfect cocoon can produce a single thread one mile long, and 110 cocoons equal one silk tie.

A tiny worm produces the textile of princes, a lowly plant grows strong, durable fiber, and a humble animal's fleece keeps us warm and waterproof. Each one is familiar, but let not their familiarity hide the wonder of design, and the fact that they exist at all. Mankind needs to be clothed — and the Creator has provided the insects, plants and animals to give us precisely what we require. Thank You!

בָּרוּךְ אַתָּה ה' . . . מַלְבִּישׁ עֲרֻמִּים.

Blessed are You, Hashem, . . . Who clothes the naked.

here are many differences between the Land of Israel and Great Britain. Some are inherent in the spiritual make-up of the land, while others are superimposed by the social habits of the inhabitants. One of the latter is the use of the car horn. In the Holy Land, any maneuver is preceded by a statutory honk of the horn. Should the traffic lights turn green, and the driver of the car at the front of the line hesitate for a quarter of a second before pressing his foot on the gas, the many cars behind him will remind him of his responsibility in a multitoned cacophony. Sounding the horn in Israel is as natural as signaling with your turn signal. On the other hand, anyone thinking of visiting the British Isles and renting a car should be warned that sounding the horn there is tantamount to a declaration of war. If you are stuck in a line of stationary traffic, and you dare to press your horn to indicate to the driver in front that he can move forward — even if it is just the gentlest of little toots — it will be taken as seriously as a slap on the face. The recipient will turn around and glare at the horn-presser as if he had delivered the worst insult. Beware!

Another marked difference is the use of *succah* roofs. In the wonderful Land of Israel, where the sun usually shines from a cloudless sky throughout the *Yom Tov*, the hinged roof is absolutely unnecessary. No one needs it, and few have heard of it. In direct contrast, any resident of England who builds a *succah* without a removable roof can look forward to a damp, dripping Succos. It is for this reason that English Jews are considered world experts in all matters of ropes and pulleys. With their formidable experience at winches, cables and hinges — experience that increases with each passing Succos — there is little that they cannot construct when they put their minds to it. Little surprise is it, therefore, to know that on the East Side of Britain, over the Humber Estuary, there is a bridge with the longest single span in the world. It is held up by two mammoth cables, each nearly 1½ miles long, and weighing 5,500 tons. The cables are made up of a total of 43,000 miles of steel wire, which would stretch more than 1½ times around the world. This great Humber Bridge was opened in 1981 after 7 million man-hours of work.

On the banks of the Humber estuary, almost hidden among the tall grass, sits a solitary spider, and laughs. Looking out at the mighty structure, where twin towers — each 50 stories high — support the massive cables, which in turn hold up the bridge, it is indeed an impressive structure. He then looks at his own little body, and wonders how it is that he, diminutive creature that he is, is able to produce feats of engineering at least equal to the grand bridge, with products so superior that the great bridge looks like a Lego model in comparison. Let the humble spider share its secrets!

Spider is to web as cow is to milk. How does the spider produce the silk that is the raw material for its web? The spider produces silk in glands inside its body. The silk, which is made of protein, begins as a liquid, and passes through spinning tubes to the spinarets at the rear of the spider's body. The spinarets move rather like fingers, spinning the silk threads. They can stretch out or be squeezed together, to make thin threads or wide silken bands. Do not think for a moment that the spider is limited in the type of silk that it manufactures. A trapdoor spider can use different groups of glands and spinarets to produce sticky silk for making its trap, and soft silk for lining its burrow. Translate this ability into a bridge technician capable of pulling steel cable out of his left ear, and you will realize that the spider embodies quite a skill.

If a spider could do nothing else but produce silk, that in itself would be sufficient reason to sit down and ponder upon the source of this great demonstration of wisdom. But the silk itself is extraordinary. It has a tensile strength far greater than steel, and second only to fused quartz; spider silk can be stretched five times its length before it breaks. You might be interested that scientists have synthesized the material from which the golden orb weaver spider makes its web. It is one of the strongest materials in the world, and could be used for ultralight suspension bridges, tough cars that never rust, and shoes that never wear out. On an equal-weight basis, spider silk is far stronger than steel. It has been estimated that if a single strand could be made about 10 mm. in diameter, it would be strong enough to stop a jumbo jet in flight! The attraction of silk spun by spiders to the scientist is a combination of great strength and enormous elasticity, which man-made fibers have been unable to replicate (try and stretch a steel cable). A third important factor is that it is extremely light.

The method by which the scientists have managed to artificially produce spider silk is difficult and tedious, not to mention expensive. In discussing the protein from which the spider's silk is manufactured, they say, "The spider mixes the protein into a water-based solution and then simply spins it into a solid fiber in one step. Since we are not as clever as the spider, and are not using organisms nearly as sophisticated, we substituted man-made approaches and dissolved the protein into chemical solvents which are then spun to extrude the material through small holes to form the solid fiber . . ." So, Mr. Spider, you are cleverer than the scientists, and use machinery far in advance of anything that our sophisticated technological age can produce — that's quite a feat. From where did you get acquire such intelligence, little spider?

Spiders suffer from being unpopular. The sight of a spider on a bathroom wall is usually sufficient to send the bathroom owner racing down the corridor in horror. Which is a shame, for spiders are true friends of man. Before reaching for your slipper to flatten the spider, consider that the spider's entire life is devoted to snaring and devouring insects which could otherwise multiply and desolate the earth. It has been estimated that each year the spiders in England and Wales destroy insects more than equal in weight to the entire human population of that area. And how cleverly it constructs its web . . .

The most impressive spider web is the orb web, that symmetrical masterpiece which ornaments every backyard and garden. The first line of silk strung up, known as the bridge, is suspended more or less horizontally. The weaver may attach a strand to a blade of tall grass, drop down with it, and then climb up to another high spot and pull the line taut. Or it may simply tilt its abdomen and spin out silk into the breeze, much as a small boy would reel out kite string. When the silk catches on to something, the spider fixes the free end. Once the bridge is up, the orb weaver drops a plumb line from one end, a lower bridge is built, and a second plumb line is fixed on the other end to form a suspended framework. Within the frame the spider strings radii, and at the center spins a mesh known as the hub. Around this hub, the spider spins a temporary inner spiral to give it a firm footing while it constructs the sticky outer spiral, the one that catches insects.

Tired after its monumental construction feat, the little spider wants nothing more than to rest, and for this it rolls a leaf and spins a silken nest inside. Finally, it strings a 'telegraph' line from the center of the web to its nest. And then it goes home and waits. Twang! When the telegraph signals that something has landed on the web, the spider hurries out to investigate. If it is not too formidable, it is eaten on the spot, or quickly wrapped in silk rope to be carried back into the den. There the spider bathes its dinner in digestive juices, for it can only take its food in liquid form.

In contrast to the symmetry of the orb, the web of the common house spider is an irregular maze that brings out the wrath and the brooms of housewives. Not so quick! This web is an ingenious booby trap that catches more than dust. When an insect flutters against one of the taut lines which support the web, the line snaps like a rubber band and jerks the victim into the maze. For a heavy catch, the spider pulls and tightens some threads and spins out more strands, hoisting its prey nearer and nearer. Amazingly, a spider has been seen to lift mice and small snakes, although the spider itself is seldom larger than a pea!

The Humber Bridge, and many like it, are impressive examples of man's technological capabilities. But the little spider, devourer of man's enemies, demonstrates skills and abilities way beyond anything man can produce. Where does all that knowledge emanate from? Who equipped the tiny spider with the machinery that bridge builders would love to emulate? Wisdom and intelligence do not come from thin air. The source is the Greatest Intelligence, Hashem *Yisbarach*, Who created this world with the wisdom that is everywhere, if only you take the trouble to look.

The spider sits in the grass, looks at the Humber Bridge, and laughs. So can you, with happiness, now that you know the secret of its great wisdom.

C hildren's games are fun, and should not be discouraged. Games are to children what work is to an adult. Of the wide spectrum of games available to the young, one of the most popular, exciting and certainly cheapest is called Hide and Seek. In this particular game, which seems to enjoy universal popularity as well as uniformity of rules, one individual stands in the corner, with his eyes closed, and counts (the rules state slowly, although it is usually as fast as possible) until 100 ("1, 2 ... miss out a few ... 99, 100"). While the chosen one is counting, the other members of the group have to hide themselves around the house. Favorite hiding places include broom closets, behind armchairs, underneath beds and beneath tables. After reaching the agreed number, the seeker shouts out, "100 — coming, ready or not!" and then attempts to locate the temporarily invisible members of his group. Having played the game before, the seeker usually knows where to look, and on finding the hider, mutual squeals of delight are emitted, and the first person back to base is the winner.

The great shame is that the people hiding cannot really conceal themselves effectively. If they hid in the broom closet, then no sooner does the excited seeker open the door than they are immediately spotted. We would like to suggest an improvement to this game, which will greatly enhance its enjoyment. The suggestion is that all participants should be able to blend into the background of their hiding place entirely. The one hiding in the broom closet should take on the appearance of brooms, the one concealed in the pantry should resemble a jar of peanut butter and a bag of flour, and the one furtively crouching under the bed should be able to simulate a pair of slippers and a *negelvasser* bowl. If the suggestion is adopted, then the game of Hide and Seek will go on for much longer; in fact, it will never end.

Those endowed with a skeptical nature might protest that the suggestion is impractical. How can anyone change his appearance to resemble brooms, jars or bowls? The very idea is quite preposterous. We disagree! Go to the animal world and there you will see that they are able to camouflage themselves to a remarkable degree. If they can do it, why can't we? Let us have a closer look.

A toad is a large frog. Should you ever walk along a wooded path and wish to see one, you would probably be unsuccessful. The toad looks like the lump of earth that he sits on — with extra refinements. On a dry day, its skin is light brown to match the dry leaves and soil. When the rain falls and darkens the ground, the toad's skin darkens too. There is a member of the spider family called the crab spider. This creature has the capability of change its color to match the flower it is sitting on. Its perfect camouflage hides it from insects when they settle on the flower to feed. Then the spider moves quickly to catch them for its own dinner. Down in the sea lives a flatfish called a dab. As it moves along the seabed, its skin color changes to match the background. If it were placed on a chessboard, the dab would become checkered. Of all the color-change creatures, the chameleon has the biggest color range. To blend in with its surroundings, and thus remain unnoticed, its skin can switch from black to yellow, from blue to red!

Let us pause for a moment and pose a question. Imagine that you were dissatisfied with the color of your skin. Perhaps you had freckles and wish you hadn't. Perhaps you had no freckles and wished you had. Do you think that standing in front of a mirror, repeating time and time again, "Skin, grow freckles" or "Freckles, disappear," would change your appearance? However hard we try, we cannot (without external means) alter either the color or texture of our skin or hair. Animals, however, can. How did they manage to learn this obviously difficult task? Is it possible, for example, that originally the toads were colored bright orange? When they discovered that gaudy colors were attracting the attention of predators, they held an emergency meeting of the International Confederation of Toads to discuss their plight. One inspired toad put forward the suggestion that they should all change their skin color to adapt to the environment. The motion was carried unanimously (with loud cheers of *Toad-ah-Rabbah*) and henceforth the toads lived happily ever after. Do you believe in fairy tales? Let us be clear. Animals' necessity to camouflage is not a game. It is a matter of survival. If they did not have the capability of successfully concealing themselves (the very best that human predators — soldiers — can do is to stick some twigs in their helmets) they must have been endowed with the necessary machinery and instincts from the beginning of their existence.

There is a small insect found in tropical rain forests called the Javanese leaf insect. Even if you chose that location for your Lag B'Omer outing, it is unlikely that you would find it, for it mimics the leaf to perfection. Its skin looks like the skin of a real leaf, green and rubbery, and even the detailed structure of a central rib and veins are faithfully reproduced. It has marks on its body to resemble holes in a dying leaf, and even its legs look like curled-up leaves. Lying still, the insect is virtually undetectable. In the same rain forest, the less friendly boa constrictor's skin does not mimic its surroundings. It is, however, highly effective at blending with the characteristic dappling of sunlight filtering through leaves in exactly the same way as military camouflage is used (or, to be more precise, military camouflage tries to copy the methods used by animals). Zebras, which live on the African grasslands where lions are often out looking for a meal, confuse their mortal enemy by their distinctive stripes, which in bright daylight can disguise the zebra's shape. In the dim light of dawn or dusk, the stripes seem to blend together and help the zebras to blend into the background. What is even more remarkable is that young zebras have their striped coats from birth, so that they can hide in the herd with the mother zebra, where the stripes of all the zebras blend together.

If you go down to the woods today to take photographs of the wildlife, make sure that your glasses do not reflect the light, as that will clearly broadcast your presence. Similarly, in the animal world, there is nothing that can give their owner away to an enemy more than eyes when they catch the light; and there is no outline that is harder to conceal than a circle. So how do you disguise an eye? May we introduce you to the copperband butterfly fish, which hides its eye in a dark vertical stripe? Just to complete the deception, this special fish has a false eye in its tail, causing the enemy to snap at its tail. Consider the following: No one will attack if it thinks it is being observed. For that reason, the pearl-spotted owlet has two black eye-shaped circles on the back of its head, so that no matter which way its head is turned, it seems to be watching you! Similarly, a silkmoth has two huge frighteningly realistic eyespots on its hindwings, which would startle any hungry bird in pursuit. Perhaps most frightening of all is the caterpillar of the Costa Rican moth, which has a rear end that looks exactly like the head of a tiny viper, with two large, scary black eyes. It looks horrific, and any creature that gets too close would receive a nasty shock. Would you not like to grow eyes at the back of your head? They would be so useful for teachers who like to keep an eye on their class while writing on the blackboard. Fine. Go ahead and try to grow them!

If you are looking for real ingenuity in disguise, consider the decorator crab. This crab, which lives in the sea, disguises its presence by covering its body with objects from the seabed. It uses seaweed, bits of sponge and mosses to complete the cover. Amazingly, all these objects are attached to the back of the crab by thousands of tiny hooked bristles which cover its entire body. Those bristles did not grow by accident! In contrast, the squid, which shares the ocean floor as its habitat, ejects a small cloud of ink, roughly the shape and size of itself, then it slips away while the enemy is distracted by the ink cloud. What equipment does the squid require to produce and eject ink, and who told it what its shape is? Does it have a mirror?

No one likes to be conspicuous. Would you like to wear a bright red *yarmulka* in a *shul* on Yom Kippur where everyone is wearing white? Similarly, animals with dark coats would be seen easily in the snow. Fortunately for them ('them' being the snowy owl, the polar bear, the snowshoe hare, the stoat and the lemming, among others), they grow a white coat to help them hide. Some are white or pale-colored all year round, whereas others change the color of their coat to suit the season. The ptarmigan is a bird which has a white coat in winter, but in spring starts to grow its speckled brown summer coat, with one difference. The male keeps his white coat far longer than the female. The reason for this is that hunters will see him before the well-camouflaged female, who is sitting on her eggs! Accident or design?

The message cannot be hidden or disguised. Animal camouflage is so clever, so cunning, so vital to its very existence that the design involved cannot be concealed. The truth cannot be camouflaged!

A Matter of Instinct

Could you imagine the following unlikely event? Everyone was delighted; the *simchah* was great. The young mother had given birth to a sweet tiny baby, who everyone was convinced looked just like their side of the family. The decision was made that the young mother would remain in the hospital for two or three days, to give herself a chance to have a rest before reassuming her household duties. At the end of the designated time, she prepared herself for departure, and went out to the waiting car. Her husband, who was driving, casually asked his wife, just out of interest, where the baby was. The devoted mother answered, just as casually, that the baby was not ready to come, it still had to have its morning bath, so she had left it to find its own way home when it was ready. The father raised a perturbed eyebrow and asked whether the baby would know the way, given that their home was some miles from the hospital, at which the mother assured him that there would be no problem whatsoever. The tiny baby's homing instinct would guarantee that Junior would unerringly join them in the near future. Happily assured, the parents continued their drive home.

In case you think that the above story is far-fetched, think again! Whoever said that we are talking about humans? Did you know that in New Zealand, there is a bird called a bronze cuckoo? Mrs. Bronze Cuckoo has the interesting habit of laying her eggs in the nests of other small birds. (Obviously, it saves on the rent.) As soon as she has laid her eggs, a hidden signal informs her that it is time to travel to her winter quarters. She leaves her young still inside the egg, and flies some 4,000 miles. One month later, the little cuckoos hatch, and they must now join their families, completely on their own. To do so, they must fly without guidance 1,250 miles to Australia, where they pause briefly for rest and food, and then across an enormous expanse of ocean without any islands to the Bismarck Archipelago, covering a distance totaling 4,000 miles to rejoin the family. The mother bird has left no forwarding address, and the babies have never flown before. Despite these phenomenal difficulties, their homing instinct never fails. If you have the instinct, distance is no object; if you do not, then you can lose your way to the back door.

Do not for a moment think that the homing instinct is the exclusive province of birds, although it is true that the achievements of birds are almost beyond belief. The tiny robin, for example, is able to navigate by studying the stars. However, when it migrates in the autumn, the sky is often overcast. It does not need to land and wait for a clear sky; instead it switches over to steering by magnetic compass, and flies unerringly over rivers, lakes and mountains. But what about other creatures, such as the most humble of all animals, the unglamorous and unloved snail? This deceivingly simple creature can find its way home without being able to see, hear, or smell the direction of its home base. What undiscovered complex compass mechanism does the little snail possess that gives it such a gifted capability?

If you think that these instincts are impressive, how about an instinct possessed by a tiny creature which compels it to undertake a journey on which its diminutive life depends — and for which it has never had a moment's training? Come to the world's largest island down under — Australia — and meet its national symbol, the famous kangaroo. A full-grown kangaroo is an impressive animal. It stands taller than a man, and commonly weighs 200 pounds. His huge hind legs, with steel-spring power, can send him sailing over a 9-foot fence with the greatest of ease (just for the record, on one occasion a female gray kangaroo was being pursued by dogs, and cleared a pile of logs 6 feet high and 40 feet long in a single jump!) and a twitch of his tail can break a man's leg like a matchstick. Yet this king of the outback begins life as a baby so tiny that he and two more like him could be held in a teaspoon! So where is the instinct?

A newborn kangaroo (called a joey) is less than an inch long (2.4 cm., to be precise), about the size of a bee. Its body is semitransparent, very much like an earthworm. Its eyes, ears and hind legs are not at all developed. The only part of the baby that is fully developed is its little hands — and for good reason — for now begins the journey on which its future life depends. Gripping its mother's fur, the young joey makes the perilous climb to its mother's protective pouch, usually making the journey entirely on its own. No one has taught it the way, it cannot see where it is going and it is nothing more than a diminutive and underdeveloped embryo. But this journey is always completed; some two million kangaroos hopping around Australia bear witness to that.

Once it has arrived at the pouch, further wonders follow. As soon as it is installed the joey takes hold of a milk gland, and hangs on with an inseparable grip. The teat then suddenly expands to fill its mouth, preventing the young animal

A mother penguin keeping her baby warm under a specially designed flap of skin.

from falling off. At first, the baby is not even sufficiently developed to suck for itself, so the mother kangaroo has been provided with special muscles by which she herself pumps milk to him. Just consider for a moment: The little kangaroo is attached by its mouth to the mother's teat for four months without cessation. During that time it cannot breathe through its mouth. How does it survive during that period? The answer to the puzzle is that while the young joey is nursing, an elongated part of its larynx connects with the back part of its nasal passages, so that air passes directly into its lungs. Thus, it can keep up its milk-drinking all the while and never choke. Such sophisticated machinery is hardly accidental, and demonstrates a level of design beyond our comprehension. It is an interesting fact that after giving birth to her little one, the mother may become pregnant again within a few days. However, she does not give birth again until the older joey leaves her pouch. The senior joey leaves the safety and security of the pouch for the first time after about six months, but it returns at any sign of danger. It leaves permanently after about eight months, and within a day the mother gives birth to another baby. *Mazel Tov!*

If instincts in animals are essential for their survival — be it the ability of fish to swim, birds to fly or spiders to construct a web — then humans need not feel inferior, for we have been endowed with a host of instincts without which we could not survive. It is quite common for newborn babies to sleep for most of their first couple of days, and not to appear very interested in food. Their intestines have not yet cleared, and appetite is limited. But then — hungry! Whether nursed by mother or fed by bottle, the baby urgently requires one skill for which there is not the luxury of time to learn: *It needs to suck!* Sucking is a specific skill requiring definite muscular coordination and expertise. It is neither blowing nor licking, inhaling or drinking. It is sucking — and without that inborn ability, the life-giving milk will not be drawn from the reservoir into the baby's mouth. Who taught the little one this specific ability? Is it any different than a computer which is programmed to perform specific tasks when the appropriate button is pressed? Everyone understands that a computer has a programmer. Is a baby any different?

Many mothers-to-be are nervous about their capability to look after a baby. How will they manage; how will they know if baby is crying because he is in pain, or because he is hungry; how will they know if the little one has had sufficient food . . .? The comforting fact is that the Designer of the World intended a mother to look after her own baby, and even with her first child, the mother instinctively knows far more about feeding and caring for it than she ever thought possible. The baby has been blessed with an instinct to cry when it is hungry or experiencing discomfort, and crying is the only way a young baby can communicate with its mother. The baby rarely cries without reason, and it is a demand for attention that cannot be ignored! A stranger will hear the cry, and using his skill and judgment will say, "The baby's crying!" His mother knows that a cry for food is different than its cry when it is in pain or uncomfortable, and is well able to distinguish between the two. You cannot beat an instinct!

Why is it that when you bring a baby into a room, or even the photograph of a baby, all the ladies present go gooey, whereas the men condescendingly acknowledge the presence of the baby, comment briefly on his facial features, and then ask what there is for supper? Could it be that ladies are blessed with a powerful maternal instinct, and gentlemen, quite simply, are not? If so, who endowed them with that instinct, without which the baby could cry for prolonged periods without anyone taking too much notice? The same Creator Who gave salmon the instinct and ability to swim against the current to return hundreds of miles to their birthplace, Who gave beavers the hydro-engineering skills to construct large and complex dams, is the One Who gives the life-giving instincts to all His creations.

Just Leave It to Us

veryone enjoys going to a *simchah*. When the festivities take place in a private house, the *simchah* is given an extra dimension. Host and hostess stand by the door to welcome the guests, who usually apologize for being so late, to which the hosts respond by assuring them that they are among the first to arrive. (This is followed by the lady guest turning to her husband and surreptitiously whispering, "You see, I told you we should come half an hour later!") The guests take their places at the table, admire the beautiful settings, enjoy the delicious food, and listen intently to the speeches. (As long as the number of speeches does not exceed the number of courses, there is a fair chance that they will be listened to!) The *simchah* proceeds happily along a well-oiled track, until finally, after the final strains of *Benching* fade away, the guests, now weighing much more than they did at the beginning of the evening, collect their coats, wish the host many more such enjoyable *simchos* in their home, and bid farewell.

What the grateful guests do not realize, unless they have themselves experienced similar *simchos*, is the amount of work involved in the evening's activities. Let us talk first about moving the furniture. In order to sit 60 people in the two interconnecting rooms, every stick of furniture larger than a toothpick has to be removed. Heavy armchairs go upstairs, the buffet — weighing as much as a rotund elephant — has to stand in the hall, the large tables have to be transferred to the kitchen, and the doors have to be unscrewed and placed in the back yard. Then you have to collect the narrow collapsible tables, the folding chairs, the stackable benches, the dishes, the silverware, the drinks and — most important of all — the little paper umbrellas without which no *simchah* is complete. By the time the guests arrive, you are ready for a two-week holiday. And then they leave, and the real work begins. Dishes to be washed, carpet vacuumed, tablecloths cleaned, doors screwed back, furniture reinstated, narrow tables, collapsible chairs, benches and tables returned to their source, and — most important of all — little paper umbrellas disentangled from the carpet. You are happy to do it, it is part of the *simchah*, but by the time you see your bed at 4:30 a.m. only the birds whose day has already begun are feeling chirpy.

How would you feel if, at the end of the *simchah*, when the major work of returning the house to normal has yet to begin, two people would suddenly appear, survey the chaotic scene, and calmly say, "Just leave everything to us. We will wash, clean, vacuum, return the furniture, everything. You just go to bed, and when you get up in the morning, everything will be back to normal. Please, just leave it all to us"? It would be difficult to refuse such a generous offer. But the cost! No, quite the contrary, they assure you that their services are entirely free. What extraordinary kindness!. Would you believe it?

You have it. Every Friday night, or whenever you enjoy a heavy meal, you cheerfully swallow a large variety of food and drink. Down the hatch goes wine, *challah*, fish, chicken, *kugel*, salads, sour pickles, ice cream, dessert, with tea and cake as an optional extra. Your stomach feels on the full side, and you feel content with life! When you awake next morning, pangs of hunger down below indicate that your stomach is now empty. Where has all the previous night's food gone? Who sorted it out — who swept, cleaned, washed? Who removed the litter and put everything away? The wonderful answer is that knowingly or unknowingly, the kindest of agents are at work, and in the quietest of whispers say, "Just leave it all to us, we'll see to everything; go to sleep and in the morning all will be done." And it is. Not only is everything completed in the most efficient manner, the whole operation is entirely free. How does it work?

Do not think of your intestines as some elongated tube looping through your body. The most sophisticated food-processing plant in existence would be a doll's tea party in comparison to the complexities of the digestive system. Most of the food we eat would be lethal if it entered our bloodstream. The intestines change the highly dangerous to acceptable, providing food for the trillions of cells and energy for the muscles. Protein in the meat is converted into amino acids, carbohydrates from the *kugel* into glucose. Without the most complicated chemical processes that take place constantly in the intestines, food would remain undigested, as useless to the body as the food standing on the pantry shelves.

Consider some of the details. The intestines contain cells which produce a special enzyme whose function is to digest protein. Logically, that enzyme should digest the very cell that produces it. This indeed would happen, were it not for the fact that the enzymes are made in an inactive form, and cannot work until they reach their destined place in the digestive tract, where they are activated by the chemicals

A meal fit for a king. But who is going to clean it up afterwards?

present. Trypsin (a substance which breaks down protein into amino acids), for example, is secreted as an inactive substance called trypsinogen. When the trypsinogen reaches the upper reaches of the intestines, it meets a chemical by the name of enterokinase which converts it into active trypsin. Why does the powerful trypsin now not digest the very walls of the intestine in which it works? That it cannot do because of the thick layer of mucus that lines the intestines. Notice any intelligence?

The average person is blessed with approximately 26 feet of intestine. This great length is required to present a large absorbing surface to the digesting food. This already large surface is increased enormously by one of the most amazing features of the intestines. The lining of the small intestine is covered with millions of minute projections, known as villi. Each single villus is ¹⁄₂₅ of an inch long, and there are 3,500 villi to a square inch, totaling 5 million in all. Each villus is tipped by special cells (epithelium cells), which, by a process which is not fully understood, absorb about 95 percent of the nutrients from digested food. (Please note that the complexity of the process by which the useful substances in the food are absorbed into the blood supply via the outer cells of the villi is so profound that even with the sum total of scientific knowledge available, it is not understood. The next time you hear scientists postulating with complete assurance about the events of 200 million years ago, ask them to explain how the villi in their intestines work!)

The amazing cells are produced at the base of the villus and then move gradually to the top. They remain there for about two days, performing their vital task of passing absorbed nutrients into the blood, before detaching and passing out of the intestines. Each individual villus is constructed like a tower, complete with glands to secrete mucus, so vital for the protection of the intestines, and supplied with a rich network of capillaries. The molecules of amino acids and glucose pass through the thin layer of epithelium cells, to enter the blood plasma. They are then carried away in the capillaries, and all 5 million villi are united in a vastly complicated network to form veins, which eventually join up to form one large vein, the hepatic portal, which carries all the blood from the intestine to the liver in the next stage in the purification process. Could you imagine 5 million dairy farms all connected by underground pipes to form one gigantic pipeline which would carry the milk to a central depot! That is precisely what takes place inside you.

Nothing stands still in the intestines. The entire length is lined with intricate sets of muscles. One group produces a swaying motion which churns together food and digestive juices. There are 10 to 15 of these swaying motions a minute. Another set of muscles produces a wavelike action; the waves push the contents along a few inches, then fade away. The 22-foot coiled small intestine is never at rest, and it takes three to eight hours to process a meal. Whatever watery gruel is left is passed on to the large intestine. It is here that the water•is extracted and passed back into the blood. That is absolutely vital. If a person were to lose the two gallons of gastric juices that are produced each day (four pints of saliva, six pints of gastric juice from the stomach, bile from the liver, and more than four pints of intestinal juice from inumerable glands), he would quickly dehydrate. (Did you think that recycling was a modern invention?) Nervous tension and some drugs can speed up the passage of food along the intestine, and insufficient water is extracted. The result is diarrhea. The subsequent fluid loss needs to be replaced by drinking large amounts of fluid. The only voluntary action in the whole process is the ingesting at one extremity of the digestive system, and the eliminating at the other. Everything in between requires no conscious thought. The whole magnificent process, of which only a fraction has been described, happens without our knowledge, and without our understanding. What tremendous kindness — what phenomenal intelligence! "Just leave it to Me!"

Advanced Weaponry

The following is not for the fainthearted. It is a tale of conflict and heroism, battles, guns and weapons. Everyone who has even a smattering of history will know that once upon a time, armies fought upon open fields, and were equipped with swords, spears and lances. These objects of war were called 'armes blanche,' the French for 'white arms,' and is an expression obtained from the bright gleam of steel blades. They were specifically designed for hand-fighting, stabbing, bashing, cutting and thrusting. One can picture, with some degree of horror, the scene at ancient battles as the antagonists charged each other with swinging blades and fearful cries, with fierce combat at close quarters as each individual tried to decapitate his foe while trying his best not to be decapitated himself . . . Not everyone succeeded.

The bow and arrow was a great advance and possessed definite advantages. The yard-long arrow shot from a longbow could pierce armor. When men fight with swords and spears, the numbers actually using their weapons at any instant are bound to be roughly equal on both sides. A greater number of men is not necessarily an advantage, because they cannot be employed. If, however, the fighters are armed with missile-type weapons, there is no limit to the number of such weapons that can be aimed at the enemy. The more men, the more bows; the more bows, the more arrows raining down on the enemy. The disadvantage is that the archers require strength and skill, not to mention great courage to stand their ground until the charging horsemen are within easy range. And you could run out of arrows!

Enter the gun. With the development of gunpowder in the 15th century, everything changed. No longer would mighty castles with thick walls provide safety for the lords and barons; the heavy iron cannon balls demolished everything in their path. Gunpowder shot out of the missile with enough speed to pierce the toughest armor, and the gunner did not need the archer's strong arm. There were, however, many difficulties to overcome before guns became really efficient. Early muskets and cannons were hopelessly inaccurate. The first musket balls fitted loosely inside a smooth barrel. As they were fired, the balls bounced from side to side along the barrel, and left the muzzle in unpredictable directions. Any slight unevenness in shape made the ball swing in flight. You had to ignite the gunpowder while at the same time taking aim, and keep it all dry in the rain. Most worrisome of all was that they had a very short range, and were so unsafe that they often burst before they could leave the barrel, much to the consternation of all concerned.

Many refinements and advances in design were introduced through the ages, such as engraving the inside of the barrel with spiral grooves ('rifling'), causing the projectile to spin as it went, and eliminating the tendency to veer in any one direction; elongating the bullets to increase their range; and using a lead bullet with a slightly hollow base. When the bullet was fired, the soft lead base expanded to grip the rifling. Advanced design! Nearly as good as a 30-inch-long little rodent whose weaponry is so efficient that it can kill a mountain lion, who is so superbly protected by its armory that it need fear no one. Who is he? Enter the porcupine.

As it enters, please make sure that you are well protected. Even though it is true that a porcupine has a placid disposition, and generally dislikes battle, once he decides to advance, nothing in the world will halt his course. He weighs only 15 to 25 pounds, possesses a six-inch tail, but he is armed with a terrifying armory of quills that sprout from his head, back, and powerfully muscular tail. When he walks, he rattles like a quiver of arrows — which is exactly what he is. The quills are hollow, tubular, and so lightly fixed in his skin that the slightest touch will dislodge them. And just hope that they never come your way. The quills are as sharp as needles, and covered with a multitude of barbs. Do not read any further if you are of a sensitive disposition! As soon as the quills enter the warm moist flesh of a victim, they begin to swell up, with the barbs sticking out more and more. (Remember the bullet with the soft-lead base which expands on detonation to increase its efficiency?) Because of the slant of the barbs, the quills work deeper and deeper into the victim's body. Advanced intelligence?

Read on! If Mr. Porcupine falls into the water, his air-filled quills keep him afloat as buoyantly as a cork. If he tumbles out of a tree (his favorite habitation), his cushion of quills gives him a comfortable landing. Should an enemy be foolish enough to threaten him, his behavior is always the same. He brings his feet close together, hugging the ground to guard his unquilled underside. Next, he raises his quills until, like a fantastic pincushion, he looks twice his size, and vigorously flips his tail from side to side. If the attacker is wise, he goes away. However, not everyone is wise. The attacker then tries to close in on the porcupine. 'Slap' — the muscular tail lashes sideways and drives as many as 20 jagged stilettos deep into the attacker's flesh. One slap is generally sufficient to drive off even a bear, but should the enemy stand his ground, the prickly porcupine advances. In order to protect his nose, the only sensitive part of his body, he goes into reverse gear and advances backwards, flailing his tail furiously. As he advances, the quills are sent whizzing. Ten quills will drive off a fox, 20 will send a wildcat away screaming in pain, and both mountain lions and bears have been killed by porcupine quills. The big worry is whether he will ever run out of ammunition! Have no fear, for he has been well designed. The lost quills will be replaced by new ones within a few months. In the meantime, he is unlikely to run short, for he has no fewer than 30,000 quills, each one a magnificent and terrifying weapon, covering the length of his little body.

Not every aspect of this amazing animal is understood. A female porcupine is only some 30 inches long, yet her offspring are often 11 inches long, larger than the newborn cubs of a bear. If human babies were as big, comparatively, as newborn porcupines, they would weigh some 80 pounds! And here comes the most amazing fact of all. Even before birth, porcupines possess quills which are half an inch long, and experts have for years pondered over the problem of the delivery of such uncomfortable infants!

Even barbed arrows and bullets have become superseded by something much more malicious: chemical warfare. The very name strikes terror into the heart of the reader, and for good reason. Here is the most advanced of technology, utilized in a manner designed to cause maximum damage, guaranteed to make the victim feel both powerless and vulnerable — just like a skunk. Unlike his reputation, he is both affable and complacent, and well may he be, for he possesses a weapon which makes chemical warfare look like a water fight.

It might be the very first time that the skunk (a small mammal 28 inches long) has confronted an enemy, but instinctively he knows precisely what to do. Let us say the enemy is an angry canine. The little skunk lowers his furry head, delicately arches his back, and with grave earnestness thumps his forefeet on the ground. Most animals know the sound, and run, but this foolish dog thinks it a foolish antic, and charges again. The skunk does not yet act. Instead, he stares straight before him, and with unblinking eyes, shakes his head from side to side. It is Part Two of the three-part warning.

Still the dog does not comprehend, and the time has come for the third and final warning. Gracefully, the skunk lifts his broad tail. Only for an instant longer does he hesitate, then abruptly he turns around and presents his rear to the dog. His strong little back arches in a sudden convulsive movement. Then, a thin jet of liquid glimmers phosphorescently in the dusk. Trees and grass are spattered by a burning spray. Acrid, choking odor saturates earth and leaves, and drifts on the air for hundreds of yards. Animals race for their lives to escape the suffocating fumes. And from afar, the skunk hears the agonized yelping of a running dog who will never again antagonize a skunk. His hide has been drenched with a powerful sulfide, mercaptan, and the fiery spray entered his eyes and was inhaled into his lungs. The poor dog will be blind for at least two days. You were warned that this is not for the fainthearted!!

Let us be honest. Who taught the little skunk to manufacture such a potent chemical? Why does it not burn itself up, and how does it eject it in a fine spray? Who instructed the porcupine to manufacture quills that expand inside their hapless victim? Who is the designer behind this advanced weaponry?

שְׂאוּ מָרוֹם עֵינֵיכֶם וּרְאוּ מִי בָרָא אֵלֶה . . .

Raise your eyes on high and see Who created these . . .!

Master Builder

Some people are handy and some are not. Approximately half of the population are born with two left hands, and the other half are adroit and adept. It is good to know in which category you fit before embarking upon any building project. The voice of experience speaks. There was once a young married couple who moved into a rather old but cheerful apartment. It was clean and bright, and served them well. All went well until the new husband decided that the linen closet in the bedroom required an extra shelf. It was the type of closet that was set into the wall, with brick and plaster sides. The young man was keen to give his wife a pleasant surprise, and also to impress her with his practical skills, and so he chose an afternoon during which she had gone out to perform the simple task of putting in a shelf.

He measured the width and the depth, and bought the wood. He clearly understood that in order to attach a wide plank of wood to the wall, neither tape nor glue would be appropriate. He was, after all, practical. Metal brackets would be required, two at each end. Positioning the heavy plank with his shoulder (after having penciled a line on the plaster where the shelf should lie), and holding the bracket and the long nail with one hand, he proceeded to use his hammer (borrowed from a neighbor) vigorously with the other. It was at that moment that his troubles began. With the very first thwack, a lump of plaster detached itself from the wall, and landed in a dusty heap at his feet. Further energetic swings of the hammer produced a gaping hole where the bracket was supposed to sit, and echoing bangs on the wall from the other neighbor who was trying to enjoy his afternoon nap. Things were not going as planned.

The hole in the wall had to be filled. With what? As practical as ever, he raced off to the store, explained his predicament, and purchased one sack of cement. Carrying it home, he stirred the mixture (which looked suspiciously like congealed *cholent*) in their almost new *negelvasser* bowl, stirring continuously with a screwdriver (borrowed from a neighbor). How do you apply quick-setting cement to a plaster wall? Back to the shop for a trowel. Nothing to it; he had watched bricklayers perform their skills many times. The annoying difference was that his cement kept falling off the trowel each time he raised it to the hole. In rising frustration, the young man took handfuls of squelching cement from the *negelvasser* bowl that was, and pushed them into the hole. They all fell out. Shortly afterwards, his wife returned and entered the bedroom to find a scene reminiscent of a building site, at the same time closely resembling a tropical

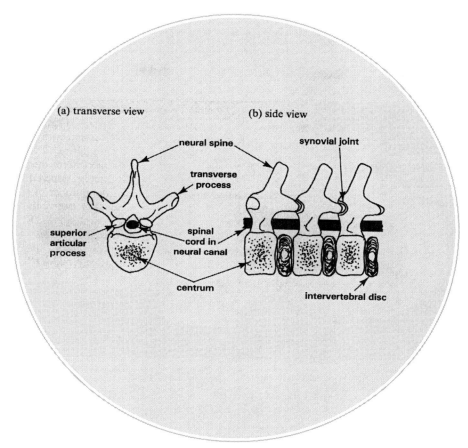

(a) transverse view   (b) side view

neural spine   synovial joint

transverse
process

superior
articular
process

spinal
cord in
neural canal

centrum

intervertebral disc

Basic structure of vertebrae

swamp, all over the once-clean carpet. She swallowed hard, closed her eyes, and walked away, with the pseudo-handyman of a husband stammering his apologies ineffectively in the background.

This category of people, who are enormously impractical, always appreciate ability in others. How, for, example, do they manage to build a roof? All the joists, the beams, the struts, the supporting timbers, the panels, the shingles, the gutters and the chimney — how do they manage to put it all together so that at the end you have a roof! This category of people, who admire practical skills in others, would certainly appreciate one of the most complex construction projects known to man — the spine. It is not one single bone, but 33 separate bones (vertebrae), each cunningly connected to the next, giving mankind stature and dignity.

The fact that man can stand erect, bend down, and swivel his head in any direction should not be taken for granted. It is all thanks to the spine performing the tasks for which it was designed. Imagine what life would be like encased in a heavy suit of armor. How did an ancient knight in shining armor fasten his shoes, blow his nose, climb on a horse, or scratch his back? The poor fellow would be immobilized in his iron prison until someone came along with a can opener. The spine has a vital job to perform in providing security for the 18-inch-long spinal cord. The spinal cord, which is a continuation of the brain, enables millions of messages to fly back and forth, directing all activities below neck level. This vital and delicate life is very well protected, with three layers of sheathing, a fluid bath to absorb shock, and a hard bony housing.

Parents, teachers, and marine sergeants are keen on encouraging their charges to stand straight. Although well motivated, perhaps they do not realize that the spine can never be entirely straight. Instead, it is formed in a gentle S-shape, a feature that is present in the spine from the very beginning of its formation, before birth. It is to everyone's greatest advantage to be blessed with this particular shape, for it is far better than a perfectly straight spine. In just the same way as the arch of the foot absorbs the constant pounding that it receives, similarly the arches of the spine act as shock absorbers. But that is not all. Every time you take a step, a jolt of approximately 100 pounds hammers through your body. If each vertebra sat directly atop its neighbor, each step would jar painfully, and the vertebrae would eventually wear away. The kindly Designer has provided the spine with cushions in between each vertebra, to absorb the impact of shocks and to prevent contact between vertebrae. These cushions are called discs. In shape, they resemble a doughnut, and are composed of a resilient jelly, enveloped within a tough cartilage. On occasion, injury can squash the cushioning disc, or rupture the disc's enclosing cartilage, allowing the jelly to ooze out. When that happens, the two neighboring vertebrae rub against each other, sometimes pressing on a nerve, causing the acute misery known as slipped disc.

Each vertebra is a masterpiece of engineering construction. Of the 33 vertebrae, the top seven, called neck vertebrae, are capable of an extraordinary range of movement. In addition to supporting a head, they can twist to allow you to study your toes or the stars in the sky. (The fact that you can lift your head up and look directly forward is an amazing feat. The only bones that connect your head to your shoulders are placed at the back of your neck. In reality, your head should always be falling forward — what is there to support it at the front? Yet the coordination between muscles and bones is so precise and efficient that you can lift your head with no effort at all.) Laterally, they permit 180 degrees of motion, allowing you to look over each shoulder. (Make sure there is no one behind you when you try it out!) Next down the line come the 12 chest vertebrae, which although not capable of such a range of movement are fully independent and capable of bending and turning. These 12 are special, for it is to these that the ribs are attached. Special provision has been made for the ribs to slot into the vertebrae, giving them anchorage and security. (Just how do you attach a semicircular rib to a spinal vertebra? You just have to see it to believe it — exactly like the structure that supports your roof.)

At the lower end of the spine are five lumbar vertebrae. These are larger and stronger than the others, because they carry most of the weight of their owner. By the way, if you are overweight, this will be the area that feels the strain most. Even carrying a modest excess on the stomach can easily amount to 10 pounds, and as one becomes older, the abdominal muscles become weaker and less able to take the strain, forcing the additional load onto the back. Do your back a favor and say no to the third helping of ice cream! People are sometimes surprised at the prevalence of backache. What they are perhaps unaware of is the elaborate system of 400 muscles and 1,000 ligaments that support the spine, and a weakness or an overstretching in any of these could give rise to pain. The spine is after all not a lever, and ideally should be kept straight. Arms and legs are the body's levers; therefore if you wish to lift up something heavy you should squat, keep your back straight, and allow your legs to do the work.

There are several amazing features of design. Although all the vertebrae are skillfully interlocked, the disc of cartilage in between each one allows for a gliding joint, permitting the movement which endows us with our flexibility. Each and every vertebra is shaped to allow the spinal cord to run through it — not through the disc, but adjacent to it. Each and every vertebra has a specifically designed opening, one on each side, to allow the spinal nerves to branch off from the spinal cord, and extend to all parts of the body. The spinal cord is like the main line of a railway track, with many branch lines emanating from it, allowing communication to the whole country. Every single muscle below the neck is linked to these spinal nerves, and receives messages from the nerves, while at the same time returning information through them to the brain. Complex is too simple a word to adequately describe the magnificent structure that permits us to stand on our feet, move our limbs, and say, "בָּרוּךְ אַתָּה ה' . . . זוֹקֵף כְּפוּפִים, *Blessed are You, Hashem . . . Who straightens the bent.*"

Spy in the Sky

When you go out for a walk today, you're in for a big surprise. You might imagine, as you stroll along the street, that no one is watching (apart from the *Ayin Roeh* of Hashem *Yisbarach*). Just how naive can you be! At the very moment that you think you are in glorious solitude, even in the open countryside, your every movement could be followed. Even when you look around, and are convinced that no one is present, you might be the focus of someone's camera. As your feeling of indignation rises concurrently with your blood pressure, and you manifest signs of outrage at this encroachment on your privacy, and you clearly indicate that you wish to show physical disapproval of the person holding the camera, take some advice and save your energy. The camera is above you. Clutching your umbrella, like some outraged major without his rifle, you jump upward to try to thwart the intruder. Forget it. The particular camera in question could be 500 miles away, far out in space!

It is a fact (perhaps disturbing) of modern life that circling around Earth, several hundred miles up, are giant cameras which can see details only 12 inches across. Some cameras claim to be so accurate that they can identify the brand name of the cigarette you are smoking (yet another reason to give up smoking!). The cameras in question are fixed to satellites as big as a 50-foot-long bus, and take up half the area of the satellites. Military commanders use these satellites as 'spies in the sky' to check the extent of other countries' arsenals. When Yasser Arafat's plane made a forced landing in a remote spot in an eastern desert, and radio contact was lost, causing some people to be concerned that he was lost, it was an American spy satellite that located him and enabled him to be rescued. Every day, weather forecasts show pictures of the Earth photographed by cameras aboard satellites.

How do the images of the cameras reach Earth? Either by radio waves, or, for the greatest detail, when fine-grained ordinary film is used, the films have to actually be returned to Earth. The American 'Big Bird' satellites have perfected the technique. The exposed film is placed into one of six re-entry capsules, which is then jettisoned, and it drops down into the Earth's atmosphere. As it parachutes down, the capsule is captured, or lassoed, in a wire loop which trails behind a Hercules transport plane. Next time you go for a walk in the countryside, just make sure you polish your shoes — there could be someone watching you 500 miles up in the sky!

It is just incredible how things have advanced since 1830, when the first practical camera was invented. The 'spy in the sky' incorporates all the technological skills available to modern man to create photographs which leave the uninitiated

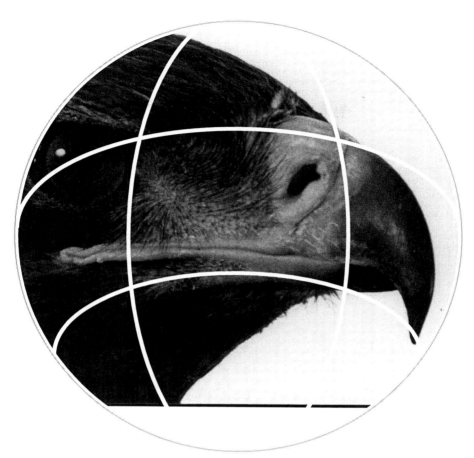

If humans had the hawk's superb sight,
we could read newspaper headlines at a distance of a quarter of a mile!

layman gasping with wonder. It is almost the last word in sophistication — almost, but not quite. The award for the ultimate in advanced design must go to the humble hawk. Let the hawk tell its tale!

The hawk can range in size from miniatures no bigger than robins to majestic giants that will attack a gazelle. Whatever their size, they have been endowed with the most amazing skills that make them almost as feared as the eagle. The eagle's eyes are so effective that he has been known to detect a fish three miles from the spot where he is soaring. The hawk, for his part, has been seen flying high over a mountain ridge, then suddenly close its wings and make a long, unwavering dive for a small bird, which it snatches in its knuckled talons. When the hawk first spotted its prey, the two birds were at least 1½ miles apart! If we human beings had comparable vision, we would be able to read newspaper headlines a quarter of a mile away, instead of trying to squint at the paper being read by another member of the family from across the table!

Much of the hawk's amazing sight comes from the size of its eyeballs, which are often as large as ours, and extend far back into the skull. In addition, the retina (the screen on the back of the eye on which the picture image is thrown before being transformed into electrical impulses) is nearly twice as thick as a human's, and is packed with millions of minute visual cells. Just think for a minute. Would you care to have superb sight? If you are a highway driver, would you like to detect a police car at a distance of five miles? Fine. Go ahead and instruct your eyeballs to increase in size, and your retina to double its thickness, ensuring, naturally, that you increase the almost unbelievably complex wiring in which every single one of the millions of light-receiving cells in the retina is connected to the optic nerve. Go ahead and try!

Flying in the sky has its hazards. The powerful sun produces glare that can distract the most conscientious of flyers. The hawk cannot afford to be distracted. To shut out the glare of the sky, its eyes are coated with droplets of yellow oil that act much like a camera filter. Not colorless oil, you understand, yellow oil! The hawk has been designed with built-in sunglasses. Just listen to this: A little sparrow hawk was seen hurtling down from a height of 100 feet, and neatly plucked a grasshopper off a leaf. Astounding as the feat was, more extraordinary still was the physical transformation that had taken place inside the bird's eye during the dive. While the hawk was circling for prey, its eye lens was working like a telescope; by the time it had plummeted to the grasshopper, the lens shape had altered to that of a microscope. Human beings have not yet been able to design a pair of binoculars that can be instantly transformed into a microscope. The hawk, which simply fulfills its instincts, has all the advanced technology that it requires.

Because its eyeballs are so huge, the brain sandwiched in between is relatively small. Nevertheless, it is large enough to incorporate a memory, and the osprey (the so-called 'fish hawk'), before leaving its nest to fly to warmer winter quarters, will strengthen its nest with fresh sticks to withstand the winter blizzards that ravaged its nest the year before. The hawk exhibits just about every technique to be seen in the world of flight, and the master flier of them all is the so-called 'duck hawk,' the peregrine falcon. The bird sits on a high perch, scanning the earth below for likely victims. Having sighted one, it takes off, wings high overhead to catch all air possible for the mighty thrust forward. The wings surge forward in a rowing motion, and then close. The falcon then plummets toward the earth like a hurled stone, sometimes attaining the incredible speed of 250 miles an hour. Suddenly there is an exploding puff of feathers, as the falcon strikes a bird with its large, clawed fist. The prey is usually killed outright. But then comes the most amazing maneuver of all: The falcon darts under the falling bird, flips over on its back, and catches the prey in its talons! Is there a jet fighter, in any air force in the world, capable of such skills? And if there is, can it lay eggs to produce the next generation of little jets?

Larger hawks demonstrate a completely different method of flight. These birds are living gliders, the most buoyant in existence, and can be seen soaring and wheeling in lazy circles. How do they manage it? Nearly every one of their skeletal bones is hollow, and filled with air sacs that supplement the lungs and decrease weight. (How do you persuade your bones to become hollow?) The wings and tail are extremely broad, providing a large lifting area in relation to their weight. As the soarers slowly patrol their territories, they coast on air currents and columns of rising warm air (thermals), gliding from one to the next. A hawk is capable of picking up tremendous momentum, simply by riding these thermal currents. An osprey was once measured as flying at

80 miles an hour in a mere four-mile-an-hour wind, and not one wing tip was twitching! In order to enable it to achieve such adroitness, the wing tips are slotted: that means that the hawk, in common with all birds that soar without flapping their wings, can spread its primary feathers apart like fingers. This capability is in reality an anti-stalling device, giving the hawk the stability that it requires. Not one hawk has ever taken a single lesson in aerodynamics, yet its design is a world beater. It knows everything! The osprey, when it rises above the water with a catch, always turns the fish's head forward, to lessen air resistance! Well, of course!

There is no limit to the refinement in the design with which the hawks — in common with every living thing — have been endowed. Birds of prey have four toes with curved claws, called talons, on each foot. Hawks have long, slim toes for catching birds in flight. The osprey will sometimes go completely underwater to catch fish; accordingly its feet have rough spiky scales and long, curved talons to make sure slippery fish do not wriggle free. Whether spy in the sky, or fearsome submarine, the hawk is a superb example of the sophisticated skills, which, if seen in the manufactured world, would win prize after prize for excellence in design. Hashem *Yisbarach* doesn't need any prizes, but we have to open our eyes, and recognize the greatest Intelligence of all.

The Printing Set

Once upon a time, when you were very little, children used to receive birthday presents. In the days when life was simple, so were those presents. One favorite was a pack of colored pencils, which, together with a coloring book, really excited the recipients. That must have been long ago! Another popular choice was a pair of roller skates, which were strapped to the shoes, and lasted only as long as the straps, which was not usually too long. If all else failed, there was one present which was a perennial choice, would suit either gender, and if the donor was an uncle or aunt who was

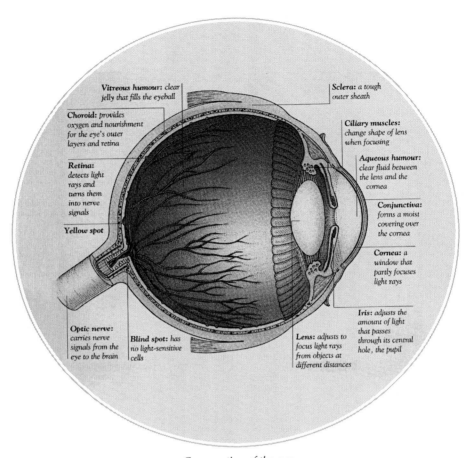

Vitreous humour: *clear jelly that fills the eyeball*

Sclera: *a tough outer sheath*

Choroid: *provides oxygen and nourishment for the eye's outer layers and retina*

Ciliary muscles: *change shape of lens when focusing*

Retina: *detects light rays and turns them into nerve signals*

Aqueous humour: *clear fluid between the lens and the cornea*

Yellow spot

Conjunctiva: *forms a moist covering over the cornea*

Cornea: *a window that partly focuses light rays*

Iris: *adjusts the amount of light that passes through its central hole, the pupil*

Optic nerve: *carries nerve signals from the eye to the brain*

Blind spot: *has no light-sensitive cells*

Lens: *adjusts to focus light rays from objects at different distances*

Cross section of the eye

not sure of the age of the celebrant (which was usually the case), this present would be fitting for all age groups. It was a printing set.

The printing set! What feelings of nostalgia are evoked by those words! Can you see it? The cardboard box, with the stamp on which you carefully placed the rubber letters, which in turn would be selected from the plastic container in which the letters lay in their pristine newness. When the vital message was complete (it was always your name and address, with the town followed by country, continent, world, Milky Way, Universe . . .), it was carefully dipped onto the ink pad, and then impressed onto the paper. Too much ink,

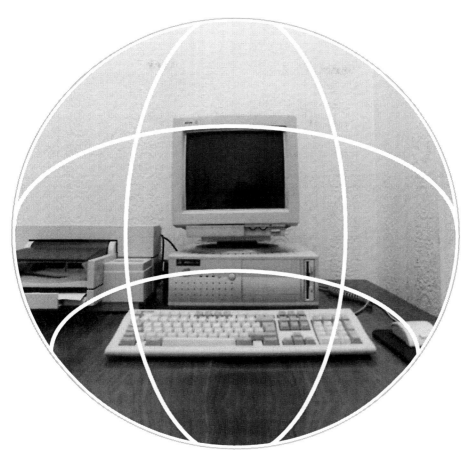

Do you recognize this? Then your intelligence is far greater than the computer's.

smudge, too little ink, faint; eventually every conceivable piece of paper, book, publication that you owned — and much that you didn't — bore the unmistakable imprint of your unique identity. After a couple of days of feverish activity with your printing set, the novelty of seeing your name in smudged/faint print wore off, and the little cardboard box would lie forlorn, or be given to a younger sibling as an act of supreme generosity.

In the minds of many people, the process of printing books and newspapers is nothing more than a sophisticated update of that childhood method. And indeed, it used to be. Every newspaper employed typesetters, whose job was to painstakingly take every single letter from a dish, place it in the appropriate line in the frame, and the whole frame would eventually meet its inky partner, and make its daily impression on massive rolls of paper. For many centuries, progress was slight, and little changed, apart from the news. Welcome, then, to the modern world. The invention of the printing press in the year 1450 by Johannes Gutenberg signaled the end of the Dark Ages, and the new dawn of disseminating knowledge to the common man through the printed word chasing away centuries of ignorance. Similarly the advent of the computer has revolutionized the world of printing. If any old-time author, designer, journalist, or newspaper producer from years past would enter the modern studio or printing office, he would not know where he was.

Join us, then, for a trip to the graphic designer. Can your mind conjure up the scene? The flustered designer sits behind a cluttered desk, with pencils, pens, paint and paintbrushes, tracing paper, glue and colored paper all vying for space. You discuss your design, he quickly draws some tentative sketches which you discuss, you go away for a week, and in the interim period, the designer sits and perspires, drawing and erasing, cutting and mounting, aspiring and hoping that the customer will be pleased with the result. What has been described is a scene from the past. Today it is different. The designer sits at a desk on which squats a large computer. This computer, with the many programs that it incorporates, is capable of doing the work of many men, much more efficiently. One of the marvels that it is capable of achieving is scanning photographs so that the pictures appear on the screen, then altering their size and shape, adding or deleting at will, and incorporating them into any design that he wishes. That particular design is then transformed onto film, which the printer converts into the finished product. That which previously took days now takes hours. Just consider the technology and wisdom, accumulated over decades, which lies behind this remarkable invention, just think of the . . . STOP!

Stop . . . and think. Think! And if you are able to think, then you are successfully utilizing technology far more advanced than the puny computer. Just consider the following analysis. You have received a colored catalog in the mail from a well-known publisher. (The production of that particular catalog, you may be sure, has utilized all the advances in the world of printing described above.) Sitting at breakfast, you glance through the catalog, remarking on the books that are unfamiliar. Those that are familiar are passed over without comment. It so happens that you were thinking of buying a relative a present, and now that you know what is new on the market, you decide to pay a visit to the local bookstore. On the table reserved for recent publications, you recognize several books from their picture in the catalog, and eventually make your purchase. Has anything dramatic happened?

Has it indeed! You were reading the catalog. What actually was happening? Images, formed from light, entered your eyes. Those rays of light were focused into clear images by the lens (which is itself held in position by ligaments), and projected onto the retina. The phenomenally complex rods and cones of the retina convert the images into electrical impulses, and send the message to the brain. The visual center of the brain then interprets the message, and informs your conscious mind of its solution. The information is simultaneously and automatically transferred to your memory, where it is efficiently filed and stored. On your visit to the *sefarim* store, you noticed the *sefarim*. The same scanning process repeats itself, in which light rays are converted to electrical impulses, to your mind, to the memory, and immediately your memory produces the file of that book, with all the information that accompanies it — the price, the author, the impression that it made on you, whether pleasing or negative, all of which coalesce to formulate an opinion — to buy or not to buy!

Back to the graphic designer. Your photographs (or sketches, diagrams or drawings) have been computerized. Do you want to know how that is done? The electronic scanner traverses the illustration and breaks down the colors into their basic elements: red, green, blue and black. Each tiny element (called a *pixel* to those in the know) is stored in the computer in digital form. By electronic juggling with the picture elements, limitless changes can be effected to the picture. In a glossy magazine advertisement, for example, a new car parked on the edge of the Grand Canyon may never have moved out of the showroom where it was photographed. Computer processing has transplanted its image onto a transparency of the canyon.

It is here that we see an interesting difference. When the electronic scanner transforms the photograph onto the computer, it is doing nothing more than you yourself do every time you look at an object. What do you mean, 'nothing more than . . .' — isn't the computer a tremendously complex machine? Exactly so, and that gives you some indication of the complexity of the machinery in your head that is scanning electronically all your waking hours (with the added advantage that all your disks are provided free of charge, they never fill, there is no loading-up time for the mind to gurgle and grunt into action as all the previous information is recalled, and no one can press the wrong button which would inadvertently erase your memory. Could you imagine mistakenly pulling your left ear lobe and forgetting who you are?!). The great advantage which the mind has over computerized image processing is that you cannot rearrange the details of the information or the images in your mind. The images of your sight (and smell, touch, sound and taste) remain faithfully and precisely embedded in your mind, and no amount of wishful thinking can change those images. Had this not been the case, no one would be able to believe any testimony given by anyone, or even believe the verity of his own experiences — for how would you know that a little autosuggestion had not rearranged the elements of the facts? In this case, that which the mind *cannot* do demonstrates a remarkable feature of its design.

Producing a newspaper was once a tedious, arduous task. Typesetting was only one feature of a difficult process. The layout of the page was also hand-done, and last-minute changes were understandably a nightmare. Again, the computer has dramatically changed life. Printing sets might be fine for young children, but the computer is for real. Everything can be typed onto the computer, columns can be swiveled around, added or deleted at the touch of the editor's finger. The completed paper, with its hundreds of thousands of letters, together with all the pictures, is transformed into one little computer disk. Complex, advanced technology? Not more than your own mind, which, when wishing to convert thoughts into speech, formulates those thoughts, adds to them, changes them, places them in correct order — all at lightning speed; and without your fingers touching any keys or buttons — and then, in a magnificent display of electrochemical wizardry, articulates those thoughts into audible speech, with hundreds of varieties of intonations, accents, languages, humorous or serious flourishes! Computer, computer, your act is fine, but if you really want design, think with your mind, there's nothing finer, and there you will find the Great Designer.

The Palace of the Queen

Long live the Queen! This patriotic cry is uttered not only by loyal Englishmen, but by Japanese and American tourists by the hundreds of thousands, who each year flock to the British Isles to catch a glimpse of the chief tourist attraction the country has to offer — a genuine royal family. No longer do the curious tourists, festooned with their necklaces of cameras, need to be satisfied simply by watching the Changing of the Guards outside Buckingham Palace. They can now pay their 8 pounds sterling and enter the sacred precincts. In truth, once you have seen one stately home, you have seen them all. Long corridors, grand staircases, family heirlooms, portraits of illustrious ancestors, suits of armor, tea rooms and souvenir shops; they are all variations of the same theme. If so, why does Buckingham Palace attract so many more visitors than any other grand residence? There is no doubt whatsoever — every single tourist thinks there is a chance that he will see the queen!

Are they serious? Englishmen know better. They know that the queen, gracious lady though she may be, does not walk around her palatial home wearing the crown jewels, not even to please the tourists. Even when she is at home, she will be closeted in her private chambers, well out of sight. What the tourists will see, however, is a grand house organized in a grand manner. Nothing is expected from the queen except to act like a queen. Certainly she would not perform any menial tasks; a host of specialists keep the palace functioning efficiently. Within the confines of Buckingham Palace you will find a platoon of cleaning staff, all equipped with the tools of their trade; a bevy of catering staff, armed with wooden spoons bearing the royal emblem; a legion of gardeners whose green fingers devotedly tend the royal gardens, and a team of chauffeurs who lovingly polish the rich metal of the royals' Rolls Royce. Equally vital to the smooth running of the palace are the maintenance men, the secretarial staff, and of course the famous guards. Each performs his task efficiently and devotedly, and the system works well.

Long live the queen! And indeed the queen bee does live longer than any of her buzzing kingdom. A visit to a hive, the Palace of the Honeybee, will provide an enormous source of inspiration and wonder, and has the additional advantage of costing nothing. Welcome to the hive!

A hive contains three distinct types of bee. The first is the queen, of which there is but one. The queen is easily recognizable, because she is the biggest bee present. Her wings are shorter than her thousands of subjects, the legs are longer and brighter in color, and she totally lacks the tools for collecting nectar and pollen with which other bees are equipped. She moves around her domain in a most stately manner, constantly attended by a retinue of faithful followers. For a bee, her life is long, living for more than three years, and her main function is to lay eggs.

The second type of bee is the drone. Drones are the males of the colony, and their task is to serve the queen and enable her to lay the 2,000 eggs per day that are required for the upkeep of the hive. They are larger than their female counterparts (the workers), and are clearly identified by their large eyes and square abdomens. A full-sized hive will not have more than a few hundred drones. Although they are few in number, they make a lot of noise, a low, loud drone, from which they obtain their name. If you meet a drone, have no fear, for it has no sting and is entirely harmless. It also has no equipment to help in the running of the colony, but is allowed to feed from the honeycombs. Life as a drone does have its disadvantages, though, because at the end of the summer months they are ejected from the hive and left to the mercy of the elements!

The vast majority of the inhabitants of the hive are the female worker bees. A full-sized hive can contain up to 80,000 worker bees, who have a dazzling array of tools to enable them to perform their miraculous tasks. Two long feelers, antennae, are attached to the front of her face, with which the bee can sense taste, touch and smell. The worker bee has two pairs of wings, which fold over each other when not in use. When they are spread out, they join together to form one large surface by means of hooks on the leading edge of the hind wing fitting into a groove on the trailing edge of the forewing. When not in use, she unzips her wings and folds them away! She has a tongue which is used for sucking up and ripening the nectar of the flowers that she visits, which, when not in use, just folds away. On either side of that tongue lie special jaws for chewing and working the wax, which is used to construct the hive. Her three pairs of legs are tailor-made for the special jobs which must be done. The front legs each have a very small notch, or indentation, which is lined with hairs, and is specifically designed for cleaning her antennae. The hind legs have brushes for gathering pollen, and a 'basket' in which to carry the pollen. Besides all this, the worker bee possesses four pairs of wax glands on the underside of the abdomen, which exude flakes of wax. This wax is chewed by the bee, softened by the addition of other substances from its amazing pantry, and used to build the communal home.

The expression 'as busy as a bee' is well coined. Within the hive, the female workers care for the eggs and developing larvae, build honeycombs, feed and clean the queen, guard the hive (for which they are equipped with a fearsome sting), process the gathered nectar into honey, produce wax, maintain the hive temperature, as well as forage for nectar, pollen, an amazing substance called propolis, and water. All this takes place within a time span of four to five weeks, the life expectancy of the hard-working bee.

Many features exist in the palace of the queen bee which seem scarcely believable. The hive is a series of hexagonal (six-sided) cells. Why hexagonal? The answer is simple: because, as mathematicians and engineers will confirm, this shape container will hold the greatest amount of honey, gives the greatest rigidity, and involves the least expenditure of wax. But who told the bee?! Of course, the mouth of the cell is slightly higher than the base, to prevent either the larvae or the honey from falling out. Within the hive, there are two main sizes of cell; worker cells — about 5 millimeters across, and drone cells — about 7 millimeters across. Now comes the problem. As each variety of cell affords just enough room to accommodate a full-grown grub (larva) of the gender for which it is intended, it is necessary for each to receive an egg according to its kind. How on earth will the queen know which egg is going to produce a male drone or a female worker! The incredible answer is that the queen never makes a mistake. She lays a male egg in each of the larger cells, and a female in each of the smaller, even though each egg is identical! That an animal can produce one gender or the other in conformity with some external circumstance is simply amazing, and bespeaks a wisdom of design which is far beyond our capability to comprehend.

Every palace must be guarded, and the hive is no exception. Each hive has its own individual aroma, and a returning worker is intercepted by the guards to ensure that its aroma matches that particular hive. If not, the sting is ready for action! Every foraging worker bee has the ability to home in on its own hive from a journey of up to three miles away. That an insect as diminutive as a bee is equipped with a brain containing a fail-safe memory, that is also capable of advanced skills of navigation, demonstrates quite some design. But that is not all. Every hive has scouts, female workers whose job is to find rich sources of nectar. If one of them successful, she fills her honey sac and returns to the hive. On arrival, she alerts the other bees, and by means of a special 'bee dance' is able to transmit information as to its scent, direction and distance. As other bees get the message, they too go out, find the source of the food, and on return perform their dance and recruit more foragers, until a considerable force of bees is in the field. Could you imagine going to town, finding a store with wonderful bargains, returning to your home and by means of a dance, convey all the relevant information concerning commodity, location and distance to your family and friends! Bear in mind that each bee lives for only five weeks, of which only two are spent foraging for nectar, yet without ever having been taught anything, in that short time they 'know' how to transmit vital information, and how to interpret it.

The guards around the palace are well armed. Their rifles are the epitome of advanced design, incorporating as they do bayonet and bullets. The worker bee has a bayonet which incorporates a hypodermic syringe. Its stinger is straight, and appears to be a solid shaft. Actually, it consists of a stiletto above, and two barbed lances below. These pieces fit closely together, and form the channel through which the poison flows. When the worker stings, the shaft is thrust into the unlucky victim and the barbed lances are pumped alternately deeper into the wound. The sting of the worker takes such strong hold that it usually resists the bee's efforts to extract it, and the bee dies. The queen, however, is an important lady, and cannot afford to disappear so easily. She is well armed with a special sting, which is curved like a scimitar and is easily removed from the wound. It is never lost and may be used repeatedly. But, although bearing this fearsome weapon, a queen may be handled without fear, for the sole function of her sting is to dispatch rival queens!

No one leaves Buckingham Palace without being impressed. We must not leave our queen bee and her palace without recognizing the incredible and advanced levels of wisdom in design, each example of which offers convincing evidence of the wisdom of the Creator.

Trapped!

his must have happened to you. You walk into the bathroom, at first not noticing anything, and then, like an apparition from a nightmare, you see it. It might be on the wall, in the bath, or, worse still, in the sink — usually black, and ominous; as large as life — a spider, beetle or moth. There are three possible reactions. The first is to give a little squeal of delight, pleased for the company, and settle down to study the delightful creature. (A variation of this intrepid type is to ignore the visitor completely, and wonder what all the fuss is about!) The second is to give a loud yell of fright, run out of the room and refuse to return until the unwelcome intruder has been evicted by someone braver than yourself. Sandwiched between those two extremes is the third reaction. You feel decidedly uncomfortable in the close proximity of this creature, but know that it is your responsibility to remove it. How?

Assuming that due to motives of pity you are prepared to grant the creature the chance to live another day, how do you remove it from the room without touching it? The following method, although not yet patented, has been used with considerable success. Materials required: a drinking glass and a piece of cardboard. Method: With the glass in your right hand, slowly approach the threatening invader. Slowly but surely, cover it with the glass. Warning: Be prepared for a flurry of angry wings, legs and antennae as the thing's 30,000 complex lenses discover that it is trapped. Don't lose your nerve, and keep your hand steady. With your left hand, slowly slip the cardboard under the glass, never allowing a space large enough for the insect to escape. That would be tragic, because then you would have an insect with a grudge in your bathroom! With the cardboard firmly covering the base of the glass, remove the portable cage from the room, and en route to the front door, ask various members of the family if they would like to observe something interesting, and watch them run! After gaining the safety of the street, remove the cardboard, tilt the glass, and move swiftly to a safe distance.

Even the originator of the above master-method will admit that it does have its limitations. For creatures larger than a drinking glass, or creatures who are not inclined to sit demurely while waiting for the glass to descend (and certainly for those insects who are able to read this chapter), more sophisticated methods need to be employed. To be sure the methods that hunters use to trap animals are ingenious, although often cruel. But that does not detract from the fact that the 'glass and cardboard' method demonstrates definite intelligence. By means of careful thought and a degree of cunning, the animal is disposed of in an efficient and expedient manner. What then would you say about the following:

Imagine for a moment that you are an insect. You are flying on your lawful business, in search of food and rest. Suddenly, out of the green, you notice two leaves, rather unusual in shape to be sure, but inviting nevertheless. The two leaves are hinged in the center, and spread out as they are, they appear to offer a safe landing place. The temptation to land is enhanced by the promise of food, in the form of nectar. So why not rest, eat your fill and relax for a while? Suddenly, a voice shouts out, "Venus's flytrap — keep away!" If you are sensible, and listen to warnings, you will indeed fly off and be grateful for a new lease on life. If, however, you insist on landing, be prepared for the following.

On the upper surface of the leaf, there are large bristles, which act as triggers. When the insect settles on the leaf, and brushes against the bristles, the 'triggers' are fired, and the leaf springs to action with lightning speed. Within one second, the helpless victim finds itself trapped as the two halves of the leaf snap shut. But wait — why does the Venus's flytrap not snap shut every time a drop of rain falls on it, touching one of the bristles? The answer is simple. It is endowed with an ingenious device. If just one bristle is touched — by a raindrop, for example — the trap remains open. It is only if two or more bristles are touched in quick succession, as they would be by an insect, that the trap shuts to catch its victim. Would you like to know how the hinged leaf actually 'snaps shut'? In the center of the hinged leaf, there are special cells, called 'motor cells,' which are filled with liquid. As soon as the triggers are fired, a message (which must be chemical) is flashed to those cells, and this liquid rushes out of the motor cells, making the cells collapse. It is this that causes the trap to spring shut. So far, from the time that the insect landed, one fifth of a second has elapsed.

Poor little insect, it either has not noticed the movement of the trap, or is reacting too slowly. After about one fifth of a second, the sides of the trap are rapidly approaching. At the top of the two hinged leaves are spikes, called 'marginal teeth,' which are arranged alternately so that they do not crash into each other as the trap closes. Because they point inwards,

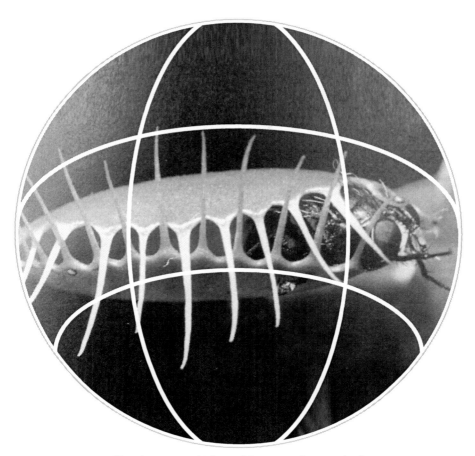

"Time for supper, I think," said the Venus's flytrap to the fly.

they mesh together like interlocking fingers, ensuring that the insect does not fall out. Even if the insect had sensed danger, it is now too late for it to make its escape. Meanwhile, as the two sides of the trap draw inexorably closer, the trigger-bristles inside the trap fold back. This guarantees that they are not damaged, and will be able to work again when the trap reopens for business.

The wonders have not yet ended. Now that the insect is well and truly caught, the Venus's flytrap can act with leisure. Using sensory glands on the surface of its twin leaves, the plant tests its victim. If it contains protein, the trap closes fully, and digestion begins. Specially designed glands inside the trap secrete acid and substances called enzymes, which will slowly digest all the soft parts of the insect's body, absorbing it into its own system. It will take about two weeks for the insect to be fully digested, and for the trap to be ready for another meal. When the trap reopens, the insect's hard external skeleton, which includes the wings, will blow away.

The amazing thing is that this insect-eating Venus's fly-trap could really be a vegetarian, like its many floral cousins. After all it has all the necessary equipment, primarily green leaves — which contain chlorophyll, the miracle molecule which enables the leaf to convert sunshine into energy. Why then does it have a taste for insects? The answer is deceptively simple. The insects it catches are simply used as a dietary supplement — they are the plant's equivalent of vitamin tablets. Many plants need this extra source of food because they grow in waterlogged ground where the soil is deficient in nitrates and other essential nutrients. (It is important to understand the significance of this statement. To those who espouse theories of development, we have here a little problem. According to them, the Venus's flytrap began life in a waterlogged environment as a harmless vegetarian plant, deficient in nitrates, and not too healthy. Understanding that a few juicy insects would be just the thing to enable it to survive, it spent the next 20 million years developing the phenomenal chemical-mechanical wonders described above, completely by accident. How did it manage to survive during that time? And by the way, have you ever seen fishermen, the sons of fishermen, grow fishing nets from their knees? Or hunters, the sons of hunters, develop rifles from their heads? Why not? It would be no less logical than a plant which develops the mechanism to catch insects from its leaves!)

There are other varieties, which demonstrate no less evidence of design. There is a plant called the sundew. The leaves of the sundew are covered with tiny hairs which produce droplets of sticky glue. When an insect lands on one of the leaves, it sticks to the hairs and cannot escape. "Fine," you will say, "an efficient fly catcher," and indeed the leaves of the Portuguese sundew are so sticky that they are hung up indoors to catch flies. But that is not the end of the story. The edges of the leaf gradually curl inwards and the insect is digested. How does the plant know the exact strength of glue to produce that will keep the insect attached? (How do you produce superglue from earth, sunshine and raindrops?) How do you ensure that the glue remains in tiny droplets at the top of the tiny hairs (the only place where they will be effective), and not ooze to the bottom of the hairs in a sticky, ineffective mess? How does the leaf become aware of the presence of a trapped insect, so that it knows to curl up in its digestive embrace? It's something to think about.

And so is this: There is a plant which grows in Southeast Asia called a pitcher plant, which enjoys an insect-rich diet. Its trap is shaped like a jug, complete with a lid to keep out the rain (which would dilute the gastric juices). Insects are lured to the pitcher by its bright color and by the nectar which is produced around the rim. The surface of the rim is slippery, so when insects try to settle on it, they lose their footing, down they fall, and drown in the fluid at the bottom. And there they are digested.

You need more brains than brawn to trap an insect. The sophistication employed by plants to trap their dinner makes the man with his glass and cardboard look like a wild native with a club by comparison. Evidence of intelligence? Brilliant design? What a brilliant Designer!

מַה גָּדְלוּ מַעֲשֶׂיךָ ה'!

How great are Your deeds, Hashem!

It was not going to be an easy meeting. The Chief had already heard undercurrents of dissatisfaction, and the rumblings were ominous. Not that you could blame the villagers; after all, who in their position would not be upset? The Chief sympathized, but finding a solution would not be easy. He was not looking forward to the meeting that night. When the sun set and the children had been put to bed, all the villagers assembled in the village hall, a long low building illuminated by burning torches. An air of expectancy hung in the air, mingling with the acrid smoke produced by the torches, creating an atmosphere of tense excitement. A hushed silence descended on the gathered crowd as the Chief arose to speak. "Friends," he said, "I know that you are unhappy. Could I ask your representatives to stand up and let me hear your complaints?" A roughly clothed man stepped forward, urged on by the villagers, and at first nervously, but with increasing passion and conviction, began to speak.

"I know that I speak for everyone when I say that we have had enough. How much more can we take? Every day is the same; Dark, dreary and dismal. They say there's no place like home. Home! How can you call it home when it is so gloomy and cheerless? It is enough to depress the happiest man! Our huts are just four blank walls. They don't allow the faintest glimmer of light to penetrate, and in order to gain any illumination, we have to leave the door open, which means freezing in the winter. Alternatively, we can knock a hole in the wall, which is fine if you enjoy a hundred-mile-an-hour wind gusting through your quarters. What can we do to let some light into our lives? It might be summer, it might be winter, it could be day or it could be night; in our lightless prisons we know no difference. Of one thing we are sure — it is always dark and depressing, and we feel like potatoes imprisoned in a sack. Chief! Help us — with your wisdom, shed some light on our dismal situation!"

The villager sat down, inspired and inflamed by his own rhetoric. A wave of agreement rippled through the crowd, welled up, and broke at the feet of the Chief, who sat in melancholic brooding silence, apparently deep in thought. This was no small problem, and he could think of no light solution. Suddenly, he leapt to his feet. "I have the answer," he said excitedly. "If we could create a substance, some material that is solid, but at the same time allows the light to penetrate, then our problems are over. We could leave an aperture in the wall, place this substance in the hole, and our lives would be transformed!" A hum of excitement spread through the hall as the villagers discussed the Chief's suggestion. Then, like cold water on rising dough, a man of cynical disposition at the back of the crowd stood up and shouted, "You're really

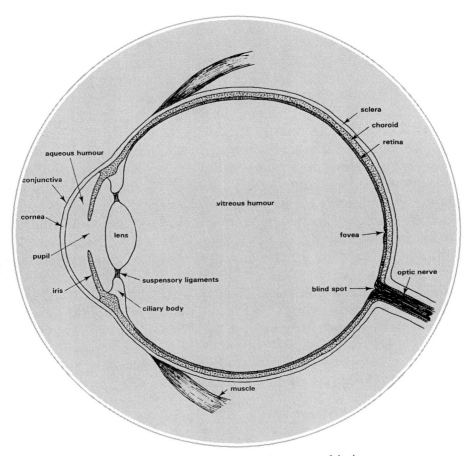

Cross section of the eye, showing the position of the lens.

great, Chief, a man of unsurpassed wisdom. How do you suggest we find this magical substance which is solid yet
transparent? Everyone knows that apart from ice, there is no
such substance known to man!" The Chief slumped in his
seat, and stared uncomprehendingly into the deepening
gloom, glassy-eyed.

Give the Chief your sympathy, for he deserves it. If you were
in his position, how would you go about inventing glass? How
do you set about creating transparent cells? It's like asking
someone to construct a transparent wooden table. How can
something exist, have a form and a mass, be solid and resilient, yet be non-existent to light waves? If you are able to

The last word in sophisticated lenses. Almost as clever as . . . your own!

read this article, you must have found the solution. You must have — because at the very front of your eyes you are the fortunate owner of two lenses. Have a look at the lens, or, better still, through your lens, and you will see wonders which the Chief could never have imagined.

The lens is transparent. That means that it is composed of tightly packed transparent fibrous cells, called lens fibers. If the lens would not be transparent, or if any of the parts of the eye which need to allow light to penetrate (the cornea, which covers the front of the eye, or the liquids which fill the eye in front of and behind the lens) would not be transparent, the eye would not function as an eye. It would be like attempting to take a picture with a camera whose lens cover was still attached. The amazing phenomenon of having transparent cells exactly where they are required (there are no other transparent cells anywhere in the body apart from the eye) is one which cannot be taken for granted — especially when the very invention of glass is far from simple. (Would you know, from your own intelligence, that glass is formed by the fusion of silica and sodium carbonate?) And the lens in your eye is far more complicated than a simple piece of glass. First of all, the lens is packaged in a flexible capsule. It needs to change shape! Secondly, the lens is flatter on its front than on its rear side. The material in the center of the lens has a greater refractive power (the ability to bend rays of light) than at the edges, and this property enables it to produce a sharper image than could a simple glass lens.

Why does the lens need to change its shape? You do not need to be a student of advanced optics to be able to comprehend. Suppose you are looking at a dot in the distance. Light rays are reflected from it and enter your eye. The light rays are bent inwards as they pass through the cornea and lens, so that they meet on the retina at the back of the eye. (The retina is a delicate layer of tissue which lines the inside of the eyeball, containing millions of sensory cells, which respond to light and send a message to the brain, which then interprets the message and tells you what you have seen.) For the image to be clear and in focus, the light rays must meet exactly on the retina. Suppose a distant object comes much closer. If the eye did not adjust in some way, the light rays would meet *behind* the retina, and the dot would be out of focus. However, the eye does adjust; and the lens becomes rounder. This bends the light rays more, so that they meet on the retina as before. The ability of the lens to change shape is called accommodation, and deserves a closer look.

The lens of the eye is not encased in the eyeball as the lens is in a camera. It is suspended within the eye, and held in place by ligaments (called the zonular fibers of Zinn!). These ligaments are attached at their other end to the outer surface of the eye, which contains the muscles which provide the power to exert the necessary pull and relaxation on the ligaments, which in turn will change the shape of the lens. The wonder is what it is exactly that provides the impetus to inform your ciliary muscles (for that is their name) that the object in question is not in focus and adjustments need to be made. The fact is that the stimulus for accommodation is the nearness of the object, but the manner in which this nearness is translated into a stimulus is simply not known! The fact that the image is blurred is not sufficient to induce accommodation; the eye has some power of discriminating whether the blurredness is required. What it is we do not know, but we do know that it works thousands of times each day, as you constantly change the focus of your vision.

Every living cell needs nourishment. The fact that the trillions of cells in the body are provided with their correct diet constantly through the transportation system of the blood supply is definitely one of the wonders of the world. But here we have a problem! Neither the transparent lens nor the nearby cornea have any blood vessels, which means that they have no supply of blood, with its attendant food, reaching them. How then do they survive? The space between the lens and the cornea is filled with a watery solution called aqueous humor. It has a composition similar to blood plasma, containing dissolved salts and glucose. This vital fluid also contains dissolved oxygen, and supplies both the lens and the cornea with nutrients and oxygen, without which they could not survive. Where is the kitchen that produces this life-saving diet? Why, it is in the eye itself (in the area around the lens) that manufactures and secretes this perfect broth. The area behind the lens is filled with another substance, the jelly-like vitreous humor, which is a protein gel, that helps maintain the shape of the eye. Where is this specialized jelly produced? Special cells on the retina manufacture this jelly-like vitreous humor, and the jelly returns the favor by pressing against the retina, keeping it firmly in place at the back of the eye. Both fluids play a vital role in refracting the light which enters the eye. (It is worth noting that wherever liquids are manufactured, facilities must be provided for drainage of excess or waste liquids. It will, therefore, not surprise you, but it should impress you to know that within the eye there is a drainage canal — called the canal of Schlemm — into which the liquid can drain. The canal of Schlemm itself empties into the venous system.)

Think for a moment. No one who wears glasses would accept for one second that his corrective lenses, each with their specific prescription, had arrived on his nose by accident. Peer into the eye, with its two living crystalline flexible lenses, transparent, suspended in mid-eye, bathed and fed by chemicals manufactured on site, granting the gift of sight, your window to the world. Do you see Intelligence?

בָּרוּךְ אַתָּה ה' . . . פּוֹקֵחַ עִוְרִים!

Blessed are You, Hashem . . . Who gives sight to the blind.

An Open and Shut Case

What a glorious day it was. The sun shone in the late summer sky, the air was warm and friendly, the open road beckoned, and the gleaming new car stood outside the front door. The fact that the car was not owned by the driver, only rented, was a detail that did not even constitute a fly in the ointment. Quite the contrary! A rented car provides all the joys of driving with none of the responsibilities of maintenance. The family, excited at the prospect of a cross-country outing, filled the car with all the essential supplies that a two-hour journey demands (i.e., enough food for a two-week siege), and settled into their seats. The driver meanwhile busied himself in the house, adjusting the thermostat, locking the windows and doors, and packing his briefcase, before venturing outside to pack the trunk. In went the blankets, in went the packages, the briefcase, and then he took off his jacket and laid it carefully on top of everything, and slammed the trunk lid shut. He went back into the house to perform a final check, and then returned to the car to begin the journey. Hands in pockets, looking for the key — not there! Where could it be? Top shirt pocket? Empty. Of course, it was probably in his jacket pocket; yes, indeed, he even remembered slipping it in earlier. Fine, off to the trunk, reach for the button — locked!

It took a few moments for the implication of the situation to sink in. The key to the car ignition was in his jacket, which was in the car trunk, which was firmly locked. It was a rented car, therefore he had no spare key. He had to open the trunk! There must be a catch inside the car with which to open the trunk — all the newer model cars have them — this one didn't. That's it! The back seats pull down, allowing access to the trunk from within the car. Simple! A quick examination revealed that this particular model of vehicle was so security conscious that you could only pull down the back seats by means of the key — the key that was now securely locked in the inaccessible innards of the trunk. As the situation became clear to the car's inhabitants, a flurry of good ideas flew from window to window. "Force the seats down; try a coat hanger; try a different key; call the police . . ."

It was an interesting yet frustrating situation. Interesting, for here was a problem that definitely had a solution; yet frustrating, for without the key they were rooted to the spot, and that key was tantalizingly close, so close but so inaccessible. Keep calm everyone! The solution to the problem took two hours to materialize. A road-service mechanic arrived, forced the back seat forward by brute strength, wedged it open with a can of baked beans (the necessary tool for any emergency), and with the aid of a metal hook and a flashlight, succeeded in removing the jacket in which rested — the elusive key!

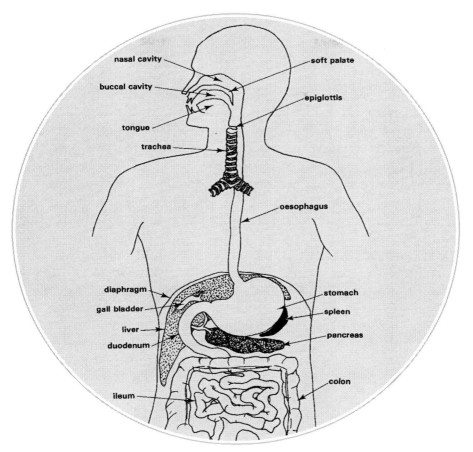

Diagram of the Digestive System

What a *simchah*! It is indeed a *simchah* when that which should be open is open, and that which should be shut is shut. Problems begin when the open is closed or the closed opened. The happiness and gratitude are very much in place, for it is by no means simple.

Prepare a delicious meal, and the grateful participants will praise your culinary skills, assuring you that the food was mouthwatering. If someone in the house is frying onions and tomatoes in readiness for their supper, your mouth waters. Your mouth waters even at the thought of food (especially when hungry)! The water that fills your mouth is not metaphoric or descriptive, it is real. It is so real that when the dentist wishes to perform treatment inside your mouth, he has to insert a saliva ejector in order to prevent your teeth and his instruments disappearing under the floodwaters of your saliva. Saliva is the beginning of the digestive process, but where is it made? There are three pairs of salivary glands, lying on either side of the mouth. Each gland is a factory, producing this special liquid for a specific purpose. Any efficient factory requires piping or ducting to transport the liquid to its required location. One of the glands lies inside your upper cheek. It is called the *parotid gland*, and the parotid duct carrying saliva from the gland runs forward in the cheek, actually tunneling through the muscle, and emptying into the mouth at the level of the upper second molar tooth. A tunnel cutting through a mountain could not be more efficient than your saliva ducts. In addition, your saliva ducts have the advantage that they open into the mouth ever so discreetly, in such a way that they cannot even be seen: efficient (producing about 1½ liters of specialized chemicals each day), essential (without saliva, swallowing food would be a painful experience and you would find it difficult to speak), designed to deliver the goods silently and reliably to their destination through the intricate pipes that open and close exactly as programmed.

Some pipes within the body have to remain open constantly, and others have to be able to close, for if they remain open, they could make life difficult, if not extremely hazardous. Open your mouth and breath deeply. You do not need a degree in medicine to know that the air that you have inhaled has entered your lungs via your windpipe. It is obvious that this airway has to remain open at all times (for that very reason it is stiffened with rings of gristle to allow air to pass freely to and from the lungs). But is it really 'open all hours'? What happens when you eat your meal and swallow your food? Why does the food not drop down the windpipe, and end up trying to find someone to help it digest in the lungs? After all, the back of the throat separates into the two pipes, both of which are open and adjacent to each other! The answer is a little flap of skin, called the epiglottis.

This little trap door sits perfectly over the windpipe, allowing the mouthful to slide safely by, prevents choking, and saves your life every time you eat. How does it work? A wonderful mechanism operates when you swallow (as you do when you eat food, but not when you breathe) so that muscular action at the top of the windpipe causes the bony area at the top of the windpipe to rise (you can feel it rise by placing your fingers on the front of your throat as you swallow), which in turn causes the epiglottis to fall over the opening of the windpipe, effectively preventing anything from entering it. For this reason, it is impossible to breathe while you swallow. The very act of swallowing, something which can also easily be taken for granted, is a complex series of neuro-muscular wonders, in which the small and humble flap of tissue stiffened with gristle — your very own epiglottis — plays such a vital role.

So now you have successfully swallowed some food. Well done! It should now disappear, as they say in drinking parlance, 'down the hatch.' Well, your food pipe is a pipe, open at both ends, so the food should just drop down into the stomach with a comforting plop. If it did, it would be extremely painful and uncomfortable. In order to make life pleasant, the food pipe contains the following features of design: It is narrow and soft, but is flexible, and can expand to accommodate large pieces of food. It contains muscle fibers that contract and relax alternately, urging the food along in a gentle wave-like motion towards the stomach. (It is because the passage along the food pipe is muscular rather than gravitational that you can eat while standing on your head!) As you eat, a valve at the entrance of the stomach (called the cardiac sphincter) allows only that amount of food through that the stomach can comfortably handle. If you gulp your food down, too much may pile up in front of this valve, giving you a mildly distressing feeling of fullness. How many times have you been told to eat slowly! Without the valve, highly acidic gastric juices from the stomach would leak upwards and attack the delicate membranes of the food pipe, with extremely unpleasant results.

At the other end of the stomach, another valve (the pyloric sphincter) keeps you healthy and happy. Without a shut-off valve, large amounts of gastric juices would be dumped into the duodenum, the beginning of the intestinal tract, which would then eat into its wall. Fortunately(!) the pyloric valve lets food through in little spurts, no more than can be instantly neutralized by the alkaline nature of the duodenum. Nothing shouts "Intelligence" louder than a valve! Now travel to the end of the intestines, where we arrive at the waste-disposal unit. It will be patently obvious that this is the last place where you would want a pipe which is open at all times. It is therefore no surprise that the process of elimination of waste material from the body is severely restricted by a powerful collar of muscle fibers, which may be opened voluntarily, permitting this vital act to be performed with dignity and self-respect. It is important to realize that in a world of accident, there is no logical reason why this facility should exist, but in a world of design, there is every reason, and we are not disappointed.

Our bodies are full of pipes, ducts, and valves. Tiny ducts take the antiseptic eye-cleanser (tears) from the factory to their eye-site, and other little channels provide the drainage. The vast network of veins and arteries provides the transport system for the blood to distribute vital supplies to the trillions of cells in the body. Without valves, the blood would not be able make the climb against gravity from the lower half of the body back to the heart. What needs to be open is open, what is required to be closed is closed, everything acting in perfect harmony, a symphony of concerted action, singing their song of intelligence to the Greatest Intelligence of all.

Down to Earth

Have you ever heard of Mr. Average? He might be you. Mr. Average wakes up in the morning, is grateful for having done so, and says '*Modeh ani.*' He then walks less than four *amos* to a bowl and cup, and washes his hands. He is not surprised to find the bowl and cup on the floor; why should he be? He placed them there the night before. Mr. Average might then go to the window of his bedroom, pull aside the curtain, and peer out. Fifty percent of Mr. Averages do so in order to discover what kind of weather is on offer in the big world outside, and groan or smile accordingly. The other fifty percent have a different motive. They wish to ascertain if their cars are still standing, unscathed, where they parked them the previous night. Car theft is on the increase, you know. Still there? Relief! His morning routine then takes him to the bathroom, where the towel is still on the rack, and his toothpaste at the side of the sink. Do you hear a mighty sigh of relief that they are both still in position? Not from Mr. Average. He then ventures into the kitchen. His cup of coffee before *Shacharis* is a must. Is he gratified to find the kettle still on the stove? Is he relieved to see the refrigerator in its customary place, and the coffee jar and cup on the shelf? I beg your pardon? This is Mr. Average — why on earth should he give these perfectly natural phenomena a second's thought! Perhaps Mr. Average notices that the security of his home is still intact, but do you expect him to express gratitude that his dining room table and chairs are still standing on the dining room floor? Where should they be — flying around the room?

Actually, yes! Why not? Why should it be that an object remains in its place after having been positioned there? What compels you to remain with your feet on the ground when you walk in the street, rather than fly through the air? Which unspoken command orders the bath water to surge down the drain with such gusto when the stopper is removed? Why is it that when you release your hold on a glass over a stone floor, it will go into a free fall with shattering results? What is the force that pulls every object down to the ground with such power?

Prepare to be amazed. For although we can give it a name, observe its impact, and even predict its effects, we cannot explain what it is. Gravity is the name of the force (not to be confused with gravy, which is poured, by means of gravity, with the utmost gravity, over meat!), and without it we could not live. It also gives us the opportunity to look at a stone lying on the ground, and observe the wonders of Creation. We know that the earth exerts a pull, which is why a stone which is thrown up into the air will eventually return to earth. It is tempting to think small. We would like to think

Wait for the crash — but what force is pulling the vase downwards?

that without this pull, life would be inconvenient. How could we live if every movable object would have to be screwed to the floor? How could you bake if all the ingredients were floating through the air? How could you learn if your table, chairs, *sefarim*, pen, and paper were in perpetual motion around your room? How could you sleep if your covers, pillow, bed, and indeed you yourself were never at rest? Without gravity you could never empty your bath! That should be the worst of your problems. For without gravity, there could be no life.

Isaac Newton, who was born in 1642, was one of the world's great scientists. He himself admitted, "If I have seen further, it is by standing on the shoulders of giants," and it was he who is said to have realized the great significance of gravity. It was in 1666 (the year of the Great Fire of London) that Isaac Newton was sitting in his garden, when he saw an apple fall from the tree. He pondered and came to the conclusion that the power of gravity (which had brought the apple from the tree to the ground) was not limited to a certain distance from the earth but that this power must extend much further than was previously thought. Why not to the moon, why not to outer space! Newton then proved that the planets orbit around the sun because there is a long-range force — gravity — which attracts them towards it. Interestingly enough, in about 1820 it was discovered that the planet Uranus, then the furthest known planet from the sun, was not moving in the orbit which it should have followed according to Newton's law. Either his law was wrong, or there was something beyond Uranus pulling at it. An English and a French astronomer, working quite independently, calculated the orbit this unknown planet would have to follow to account for the disturbance in the orbit of Uranus, and told the astronomers where to look for it in the sky. Thus the planet Neptune was found in 1846, and Newton's law was vindicated. In 1930, a very small and distant planet beyond Neptune was discovered in much the same way, and named Pluto.

Think big! Gravity keeps the planets in orbit around the sun (together with all the numerous satellites which encircle earth) and holds stars together in immense groups called galaxies. We must not think in terms of the absence of gravity making life inconvenient by having to chase the toothpaste with a butterfly-catcher's net, but rather in terms of reality. Without gravity, there could be no life. Without this phenomenal force called gravity, the galaxies and the planets, the stars and the constellations would be flying around in complete disarray. Nothing in the vastness of the universe could survive for too long. It is gravity which locks the earth in its precise distance from the sun. That distance is 93 million miles. Any closer, and we would burn; further away, and we would freeze. We depend on gravity for our very survival.

Nothing is unimportant. Every single particle exerts a gravitational force. Even an apple pulls with a small force. But the earth's pull is so much stronger that the apple falls down towards the ground. Two large ships floating in close proximity to each other will draw inexorably closer, each one drawing the other by its own gravitational pull. The larger the object, the stronger the pull. The sun is a million times larger than the earth, and so is able to exert its gravitational influence over vast distances. The moon, on the other hand, is much smaller than earth, so its gravitational force is commensurately weaker. Gravity on the moon is about one sixth that on earth, enabling you to jump about 15 feet high the next time you visit. The moon's gravitational pull is sufficiently strong to be felt down here at home. The rise and fall of the tides is caused by nothing other than the moon! The oceans on the side of the earth nearest to the moon are pulled outwards by the force of the moon's gravity, creating a high tide. At the same time, a high tide occurs on the opposite side of the earth because the moon's gravity is less there, and the water bulges away. The sun has a lesser effect on the earth's water, but when the moon and the sun are in line, at the new or full moon, their forces combine to produce extremely high or low 'spring' tides. Who would have thought that when you go to the beach to build your sand castles, the tide-in or tide-out factor would be influenced by the invisible moon!

And here lies the wonder. Long before the falling apple inspired Newton to investigate the effects of gravity, anyone who broke a glass or dropped a stone into a pond was aware that some kind of force makes things fall to earth. Everyone takes gravity for granted, yet of all the natural forces, it is the one that scientists know least about. Physicists can happily describe the other three basic forces in the universe. These are electromagnetism (which is much stronger than gravity — to be precise, 100 million million million million million million times as strong — as the metal pin which defies gravity by jumping up to the little button magnet demonstrates), and the 'strong' and 'weak' nuclear forces. All three operate inside atoms and each force governs a particular kind of activity within the atom. One mathematical theory covers how these three forces operate. But that theory does not describe gravity, and scientists cannot say what gravity 'is made of' in the way they can describe what happens inside an atom. By comparison to the other three, gravity is so, so weak, yet it extends across the universe and acts on a vast cosmic scale! Here you have a massive paradox. The cleverest people in the world know exactly what gravity does, and can predict its effects with extreme accuracy. But they do not know what it is. The most familiar of the forces governing the universe remains the most mysterious.

Why should it be that your shoes are attracted to the earth, the moon to the earth, the earth to the sun, and all the galaxies to each other! The frontiers of science and the accumulated treasuries of knowledge can offer no answer. It is humbling for us to know that the simplest of discernible physical forces is at the same time so sophisticated that the modern mind cannot fathom its wisdom. And yet it is there, the constant force that allows the Universe to function, and we, its inhabitants, to live normal lives. Once we recognize it, it is our duty to be grateful. Can you think of anything more indicative of the Grand Intelligence of the world than the amazing force of gravity?

תּוֹלֶה אֶרֶץ עַל בְּלִימָה - חַי וְקַיָּם נוֹרָא וּמָרוֹם וְקָדוֹשׁ!

He hangs the earth on nothing,
Living and Enduring One, Awesome, Exalted and Holy!

"And don't forget your passport," shouted the concerned mother to her son who was packing his suitcase. "Of course I won't!" responded her beloved child, eyes rolling heavenwards. It was actually the fourth time his mother had reminded him. As the moment of departure arrived, and the young man was walking to the taxi, yet a further anxious ". . . Are you sure you've got your passport?" was heard from the direction of the front door. Although you can feel for the son, you know that his mother is right to be concerned.

Have you ever left your passport behind? (Like the man who said to his wife as they were approaching the airport, "I wish I had brought along the grand piano!" His wife looked at him in astonishment. "Why is that?" she asked. Answered he, "Because our passports are on top of it!") The feeling of despair combined with panic need not be described. What actually would happen if you approached the gate leading to the departure lounge minus your precious passport? The official would politely ask you for your document, and you would apologetically inform him that you had left it at home. He might look at you quizzically, and ask you to step aside. There and then he would inform you firmly that without a passport you cannot go through the gate. Being a resourceful person, you assure him that you do possess a valid passport ("Phone the embassy if you don't believe me . . ."); that you are not wanted by Interpol ("I always return my library books on time, and have never received a parking ticket!") and that you desperately need to complete your journey ("My Aunt Golda will be waiting for me!"); and you think that the steely official will then melt with compassion, and say with a half-stern half-smile, "That's okay, you can go through, just don't be so forgetful next time." Forget it! He will not let you through. You can huff and you can puff, you can bluster and blow, the guardian of the law will not let you go. Next time, listen to your mother: "Don't forget your passport!"

How often do you travel? Some people are frequent travelers, and use their passports up to ten times a year. Most might use their travel documents once each year, and many never travel! There is an organ in the human body, more precious than any passport, used many times each day, which, among its many jobs, produces a life-sustaining substance which works amazingly like the passport described. It is the size and shape of a large dog's tongue, 6 inches long and grayish pink in color, weighs not more than 3 ounces, and sits in your abdomen, just behind your stomach and in front of your spine. May we introduce the pancreas.

Every body has trillions of cells. Each and every one of those cells needs to be nourished to remain alive. The fuel

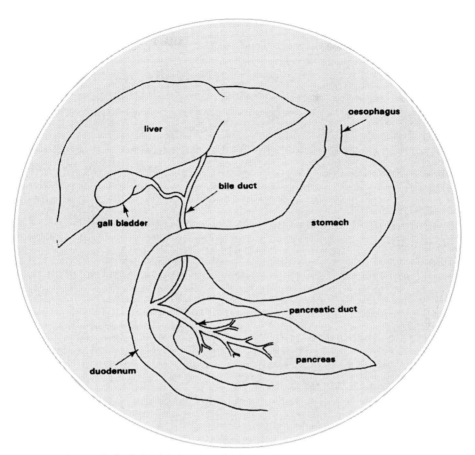

Anatomical relationship between the liver, gall bladder, pancreas, stomach and small intestine (not drawn to scale)

that they use is called glucose, and every cell is in fact an efficient furnace which burns glucose to generate energy. The main supply of the fuel glucose is to be found in carbohydrates, that group of foods which includes sugar, bread, potatoes, cereals and plant foods. The carbohydrates are broken down during digestion, and the glucose contained therein enters the blood supply, raising the blood-sugar level. This glucose must find its way into the trillions of cells throughout the body in order to provide each cell with its energy source. It cannot do it by itself. The blood sugar (glucose) cannot cross from the blood into the cell without a passport. It desperately requires this passport to assist it in making the transition from blood to cell. Without the passport, it will remain in the blood, and the cells will have to obtain their energy source from elsewhere in the body. Enter the pancreas. As the blood flows through the pancreas, a message is transmitted to the pancreas to produce the essential passport. The passport is insulin.

Scattered throughout the 3-ounce pancreas are approximately one million tiny factories. Each one is independent and is called an Island of Langerhans. This tiniest of factories is composed of three types of cells — alpha, beta, and delta. Insulin is produced by the beta cells, and the total bulk of all one million islet factories is 1.5 percent of 3 ounces! A high blood-sugar level passing through the pancreas stimulates the beta cells in the million Islands of Langerhans to produce insulin. (Think — how? What is the method of communication between the blood and the pancreas? If it is chemical, how does it work? Why is it only the beta cells that are stimulated?) There are no pipes or channels to transport this vital substance, for, like all hormones, it is released directly into the blood. As the insulin passes around the body in the blood supply, remarkable things begin to happen. The passport has arrived. In the presence of insulin, glucose can cross into the cells, they now have their energy source, and the blood-sugar level consequently falls. In the presence of insulin, any excess glucose is taken up by muscle cells, and stored for future use as a substance called *glycogen.* Insulin enables excess glucose in fat cells to be converted to fat, and stored. Liver cells are very permeable to glucose, and do not need the help of insulin to absorb it. However, insulin has a vital task even in the liver, for it increases the amount of another enzyme found in liver cells. (An enzyme is a special type of protein that controls a chemical reaction in the body. There are hundreds of types of enzymes to regulate different aspects of the body's chemistry). This enzyme (called *glucokinase*) in turn adds phosphates to glucose so that it cannot break out of the liver. Thus, the insulin acts to trap glucose inside the liver. And you are worried about one passport to allow you through one gate — here is a minute quantity of a chemical which acts as a passport to millions upon millions of cells!

What happens on a fast day, when your intake of carbohydrates is nil, the blood-sugar level is subsequently low, and your cells are desperate for fuel? Try telling them that the fast will be over in 12 hours, and would they be kind enough to hang on till then — they need fuel *now*! Cells lacking glucose cannot function properly! Witness another miracle, this time in reverse. As the blood passes through the pancreas, the pancreas 'knows' (Again, think how? What is the means of communication?) that the glucose level is low. This time it is the alpha cells in the million Islands of Langerhans that are stimulated. The alpha cells produce another hormone called *glucagon*. Glucagon in turn enters the blood stream, and stimulates the mobilization of glucose and other vital ingredients from their storage depots. The liver is commanded to release the stored glycogen and convert it into blood glucose, and the wonder hormone also promotes the release of fat stored in tissue, providing vital ingredients for the cells. All these actions are opposite to those of insulin, and the result is that the glucose level rises in the blood, and energy fuel is restored to the cells. Just consider the phenomenal system which ensures that the correct cells of the Islands of Langerhans are stimulated, and consider what would happen if the lines of communication became confused, causing the wrong hormone to be secreted! In fact, the insulin-glycogen system is a powerful fast-acting mechanism for keeping the blood-sugar level normal. One reason why this is so important is that brain cells are completely dependent upon a continuous supply of glucose, because they are normally unable to utilize any other nutrients as fuel. Any fast-acting mechanism on which the health of the brain depends does not sound too accidental!

It is interesting to note that as recently as 1969, medical textbooks were advising their readers that there was a third group of cells in the tiny islands of the pancreas, the delta cells, 'the function of which is not known.' It has now been discovered that the delta cells produce a hormone which inhibits growth, ensuring that we don't continue growing into giants. It is always interesting to note that the human body, in common with all of creation, is so vastly complicated, such a masterpiece of bio-engineering, that we attempt in vain to plumb the full depths of its complexity and wisdom.

Aside from the vital task of maintaining the correct balance of blood sugar, the pancreas has other roles, too. It produces about two pints of digestive juices each day. That's 32 ounces from a 3-ounce gland! When your food leaves your stomach to begin its long journey along the intestines, it is a highly acidic semiliquid paste. This acid (which is vital in starting the breakdown of proteins) could spell disaster further along the digestive tract — eating away the delicate lining of the small intestine — and so we need alkaline juice to neutralize it, and quickly! Enter the pancreas. As soon as you sit down to dinner, thousands of factories in the pancreas receive a signal from the nervous system to begin manufacturing alkaline juices. As the factories move into top gear, the juice flows down the specially designed duct which opens into the duodenum, the beginning of the intestine. In order to make things even more efficient, as soon as the food leaves the stomach, the duodenum starts manufacturing a hormone called *secretin*, whose chemical message via the blood stimulates the pancreas into peak alkaline production. Rather like dialing the taxi after you have ordered it, just to make sure that it is on the way!

Little pancreas, a diminutive flap of skin, unseen and largely unknown, plays a commanding role in maintaining our good health. It is a giant of sophistication, producing vastly complicated chemicals and hormones, with more than a million factories giving us a passport to life, in just 3 ounces. What an Intelligence!

If you wish to qualify as a philosopher, it is necessary to train yourself to think — not just to think the usual thoughts, for anyone can do that, but to think profound and original ideas. Many people ponder about their situation in life, and as they count their blessings, they are grateful for the things that they have, and for what they are. That's normal. To be a genuine philosopher, however, you have to train yourself to think, and thank, for the things that you are not. For example, if you tip the scales at over 280 pounds, then your heart should overflow with gratitude that you are not a ballet dancer. If you are a ballet dancer, perhaps you should have a word with your career adviser! If you are one of those people who are scared of heights, whose stomach performs acrobatics when looking over a banister, be forever grateful that you do not have to earn a living by crossing Niagara Falls on a tightrope. The trip might do you no good. And if you have been blessed with one of those voices that cracks windows, and your vocal efforts make people think that someone heavy is standing on your toe, be pleased that you are not a *chazzan*. (If you are, just carry on your good work!) There is one thing for which every human being needs to be forever thankful. Be happy that you are not a wooden spoon.

Professional cooks and chefs know that without a wooden spoon, no meal could succeed. The wooden spoon stirs the soup, it prevents the ingredients catching and burning, it circulates the gravy around the meat, it submerges the loaves of gefilte fish bobbing in the seething juice, it mixes the potatoes and meat that comprise the goulash — and, most important of all — with a chef's flourish, it enables you to taste your concoction with a tiny sip from the tip of the spoon. Imagine it was you, and the tip of the spoon was the tip of your finger. The pain, the burn, the singe, the cut would be unbearable. Imagine having to plunge your hand into boiling soup to stir the ingredients. It is agonizing to think of it. Yet the spoon, faithful servant, allows itself the fiercest treatment, the most rigorous of tasks, without demur. Why does the wooden spoon feel no pain, but your fingers do? Why would your hand burn, but not the wooden implement? (By the same token, why, when wishing to test the temperature of hot water, do you not dip your hair into it? Why is cutting your hair or nails not an agonizingly painful experience, and how can you bear to brush your teeth? After all, you are fearful of scratching your skin!) Knowing that your fingers have nerves is a tiny fraction of the story. Prepare to meet one of the wonders of the world, your very own fingers.

It is very likely that you take your fingers for granted. They are where they are supposed to be, you use them whenever you want, and you probably feel quite attached to them. It is

Focus on the fingers dancing over the keys — emunah at your fingertips

interesting to know that engineers have tried for many years to build machines that mimic the human hand. They have tried in vain. None of these devices has come close to our range of movements, and it is impossible for scientists to match the control systems of the human body. Robot machines on assembly lines can carry out certain simple tasks in a tireless fashion. But a robot welder-arm cannot spray paint, and a robot suction-grab cannot tighten screws. Each device is designed to do only one or a few of the multiple tasks that our hands can do. Think for a moment of the many skills required in tying shoelaces, winding up the straps of *tefillin*, or just opening the pages of a book. Did you know that the bones, joints and muscles in the arm and hand are smaller and finer the further down the arm they are — from your shoulder to your fingertips? This arrangement is a special design to enable you to perform much more precise movements with your fingertips than with your shoulder. The human hand is a marvelous device. Let us examine some of its features.

Intelligence will tell you that any device used for measuring temperature is a purposeful machine. In our hygiene-conscious age, many kitchens are equipped with food thermometers to ensure that the food remains at a temperature which will not endanger your health. The thermometer consists of a metal probe (which you spear into the poor food), attached to an electronic meter with a display panel. Would you entertain the suggestion that your 'last word in food technology' is a haphazard hodgepodge of bits and pieces, or would you be happier to know that it is 'designed by the experts, with safety and durability as the primary criteria'? Take a look at your fingers. Should you wish to know if the electric kettle is still warm, what would you do? You would reach out and lightly touch the kettle with your fingers. A mother who suspects her child of having a fever would rest the back of her hand lightly on his forehead. Instantly you have your information. Had you touched the kettle, or the forehead, with your nail, hair, or shoe, not to mention a wooden spoon, you would be none the wiser. Why are your fingers different?

In just the same way that the pavement on the street covers a maze of pipes, cables and channels, so does our skin cover a vast network of millions of microscopic sensors. These microscopic sensors in the skin are at the nerve endings. They are specially designed to convert physical sensations into tiny electrical nerve signals. When the sensors are pressed, vibrated, or stimulated by heat or cold, they generate nerve signals that flash to the brain. Here you have your thermometer-probe, in every single aspect superior to the latest model obtainable on the market. (Your expensive probe would not be able to simply touch the kettle to register the temperature, it would have to be inserted inside, and then probably blow a fuse because of the steam!)

Our sense of touch is far more complicated than it might seem. Although we might think of touch as a single sense, there are a number of different types of touch sensors, each of which delivers a different pattern of nerve signals. The different sensors (tucked in your very own fingertips, as well as other parts of the body) give us a wide variety of information about objects, such as their hardness, wetness and surface texture. Your Pacini's endings (named after the gentleman who discovered them) are set deep under the surface, and react to heavy pressure. Merkel's endings, nearer the surface of the skin, respond best to medium pressure. Meissner's endings respond well to light pressure and small fast vibrations. (Test yourself for the least amount of pressure that will register on your finger. Try a feather or a thin elastic band — and then tell yourself that you're not a sensitive person!) And finally we have Ruffini's endings, which look like little almonds waving around on top of a string, which sense changes in temperature. All this besides the free nerve endings which register pain when activated. Be grateful that you have no free nerve endings in your hair, nails or teeth! Listen to this sophistication. Should the pressure become too much for you, the brain will obligingly refrain from informing you of its presence. For example, if you are wearing socks, can you feel how high they reach on your legs without looking? Perhaps not. You did feel the socks when you put them on, but the feeling soon fades. This specially designed refinement is called 'habituation,' and it dulls your senses to a continuing stimulus. Don't worry, you will become aware of your socks when they change position.

Your fingertips are a gold mine. Just beneath the surface there are tiny factories (called *sebaceous glands*) which manufacture *sebum,* a natural oil. This substance mingles with the sweat which is also produced under the skin, and then spreads over the skin surface, helping it to stay supple and water-repellent. A drop of water which falls on your hand will remain as a rounded blob, repelled by the waterproof skin. In fact your skin is 'showerproof' rather than waterproof, for after a long soak in the bath, the sebum is washed away. Water can then penetrate into the skin, making it soggy and wrinkled. If you wash and dry your hands, and then try and pick up a pin, it will be difficult, because you have washed away the film of sweat and sebum that covers your fingertips. It is this sticky film which coats the swirling ridges on your fingers that helps you grip objects. The impression of the sebum-soaked whirls and ridges are your very own unique fingerprints.

Nothing is simple or haphazard in the designed body. Even a simple sweat gland is nothing less than a factory beneath the skin, which manufactures perspiration, and then at a given signal from the brain, pumps it up to the skin surface through a specially constructed channel (pore). Next time you are taking a test, and after an hour's writing you find that your pen becomes slippery due to the perspiration emitted by your nervous fingers, sit back and relax and wonder at the marvels of Creation that you are witnessing in front of you.

Look at fingers holding knitting needles clicking furiously; observe the frenzied fingers of an experienced typist whirring over the keyboard; focus on the lightning fingers of a piano virtuoso dancing over the keys — think of the action of the muscles in the arm which are activating the tendons in the fingers, think of the electrochemical activity in the nervous system flashing down from the brain for every minimovement, and think of the bundle of miracles contained in your fingers. The human hand is powerful yet delicate, adaptable yet precise. There is no device in the whole world of animals or of machines that is quite so versatile. Think of your design, think of their Designer, and you have *emunah* at your fingertips.

The Living Lamppost

Come, we are going to visit the small village in rural Russia where your great-grandfather grew up. Hop into the time machine, and back we travel to the last century. Warily, you step out of the machine and look around. It's so quiet! Noises of animals and birds assail your ears, and the silence of pre-industrialized suburbia predominates. Walking through the village, you notice the drabness of the buildings — everything looks so old and run down — and the mud is everywhere. No paved roads, no drains or gutters, just a muddy path shared by humans and the animals which are such a major part of rural life. With a childlike sense of wonder, you meander through the village, looking into the farms, the schoolroom, the general store, observing the strong faces, cosmetic-free, but full of character. You notice the rough, unadorned clothing, patched and worn. Life is simple and hard, but satisfying. The short winter day draws to a close, and the early dusk envelops the brown street with its huddled low-built wooden houses. Nighttime falls, and the whole village descends into darkness. Here and there a pool of light from an oil lamp spills into the street; otherwise there is not a glimmer. Gingerly you walk, not knowing where you are going, feet slipping and unsure in the grooved path. As night deepens, the blackness intensifies, and you wonder how the inhabitants manage to get about. They don't. The blackness of the night imprisons everyone in their homes. Not a gas lamp, not a glimmer or a spark, to break the barrier of blackness. Suddenly you feel a great wave of yearning — a longing to be back in a society which is illuminated and bright, where electricity brightens your night and guarantees your freedom of movement. It's time to come back to today!

To the age of brightness! What could be more modern? If you can remember the lamplighter who went around with his ladder to 'windup' the gas lamps, tell nobody your age! Today, no one winds up, no one sets a time switch, no one pours in the oil. At dusk and dawn, millions of street lights turn themselves on and off with no human interference at all. Do you know how it works? With a pecu! A pecu is the acronym for a photoelectric control unit, which operates a switch in the electrical supply to the lights. There, up above, on the street lamp, lies a photocell. The photocell contains a compound (cadmium sulphide or silicon) which is sensitive to light. As dawn rises, light falling on the photocell causes electrons to flow from one atom to the other, conducting electricity to the switch and turning it off. At the other end of the day, as darkness falls, the electrons in the compound become immobile, the current stops, and the lights are turned on. Brilliant! No matter how early darkness falls, the lights will faithfully switch on, thanks to the advanced technology

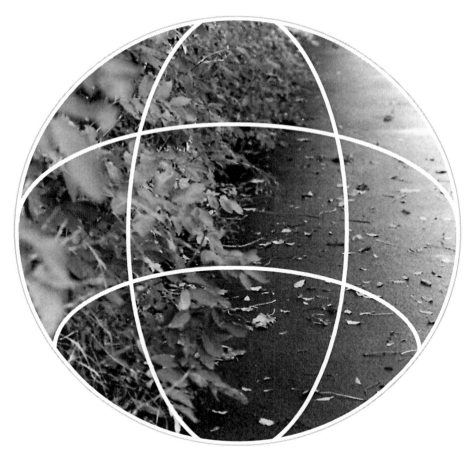

Who told the leaves that it's time to fall?

of our modern times. As far as street lighting is concerned, the 'good old days' were not so good.

Shh! I hear someone laughing. Shh! I hear it again! Who is it? A leaf? Why are you laughing — what are you saying? I don't believe it! The leaf is saying that his technology is so complex that it makes our most modern street lamps appear primitive in comparison. Could you explain?

One word for 'autumn' is 'fall.' The reason is not hard to discern. When the days become shorter and the temperature begins to fall, millions of trees shed their leaves. The falling of the leaves of the deciduous trees (deciduous refers to plants and trees that lose their leaves in autumn, forming new ones in spring) gives the season its distinctive name. Certainly, it is a spectacular process. The leaves of these trees turn a brilliant red and gold, providing a festival of color which has become a major tourist attraction in many parts of America. Beautiful it certainly is. What it is that makes the leaves fall from the tree? How is it that the twigs do not descend with the leaves? Why is it that the evergreen trees do not see the need to drop their leaves? And then we come to the most enigmatic question of all. How do the trees know when it is time to dispense with their leaves? What is the timing device that triggers the mechanism and starts the process? Prepare to hear some answers that will amaze you.

First the 'why' and then the 'how.' The enormous surface area of leaves on a deciduous tree convert sunshine into energy. They also draw water from the roots (by a brilliant process called osmosis). A great deal of water evaporates into the atmosphere from the leaves, which is fine as long as the supply of water in the soil is plentiful. In winter, however, the ground freezes, and the roots cannot take up water from the soil. A plant whose roots are in frozen soil is as short of water as a plant in a dry desert. The last thing that the tree needs is a drain of water through evaporation via the leaves, with no replenishment through the roots. Dropping the leaves enables the tree to survive. As winter sets in, the tree becomes dormant; it simply goes to sleep. Good night, tree!

How, though, does the leaf actually fall off? At a given signal (more about that soon), special cells begin to grow across the leafstalk at the point where it is attached to the twig. This creates an area of weakness across the base of the leafstalk from the outside inwards. The natural 'glue' by which the packing cells are normally stuck together dissolves. The biochemical processes that normally take place within the leaf stop, the chlorophyll that gives the leaf its distinctive green color breaks down and disappears (scientists are not sure what happens to the chlorophyll once it starts to decay), leaving the other pigments of yellow and orange which were there all the time. Eventually, only the veins are running through, and the leaf loosens. Before it falls off, something incredible happens. The leaf contains many desirable minerals. Before dropping to the ground, the leaf transfers those minerals into the tree, where they are stored for the new generation of leaves, due in spring. At the same time, the tree contains many undesirable toxins which it does not require. These toxins are shunted to the leaves prior to their downfall, giving the tree the perfect process of elimination! So much wisdom in a 'simple' leaf! Will the departure of the leaf not leave an open abrasion on the twig? Not at all. As the leaf loosens, a layer of cork develops under the area of weakness, effectively sealing the injury. The demonstrations of intelligence stagger the imagination!

But how does the tree know when to begin all these many complex processes? Who whispers into its bark that autumn is approaching? You might like to know that hundreds of millions of dollars have been spent on trying to answer this question, so far without complete success. It simply is too complex! There are, however, certain things that we do know. Every leaf, whether on a plant or on a tree, contains a chemical called *phytochrome*. This chemical is sensitive to light, and is crucial in activating the many processes that occur within the plant. Every species makes a slightly different use of the chemical messages that it receives from its phytocrome. The experts have admitted that it is highly likely that the phytocrome in the leaves of the tree, being the photosensitive cells of the tree, react to the lessening of light as the days shorten, and it is their chemical message that triggers the mechanism that results in the dropping of the leaves. Indeed, it has been discovered that trees that stand next to lampposts retain their leaves for longer periods than trees of the same species which stand away from the extra source of light. So there you have it. We walk along the street and consider our lampposts the last word in sophisticated technology. There they stand proudly, the result of decades of research and scientific development. They even have photosensitive cells. Well may the humble tree laugh. He has been endowed with these sophisticated skills since he was created, and much more besides! To quote the words of one expert botanist, "Placed next to a tree, the streetlamp appears primitive, almost naive, by comparison!"

You know what a hormone is. It is a chemical messenger. As autumn approaches, our humble tree produces a special gaseous hormone called *ethylene* which, in its complex chemical way, breaks down starches and produces sugars (apple growers use this chemical to encourage the tree to ripen its apples), encourages leaf-drop, and enhances the cork layer which forms at the base of the leaf. And you thought that leaves falling in autumn happened by itself — just pretty colors! (Who told the tree that cork is beneficial for healing wounds, and how do you produce cork from soil, sunshine and rain?)

How do the evergreens manage? They have small, thick-skinned leaves, whose relatively small surface area prevents significant loss of moisture. Alternatively, their leaves have been designed with a waxy upper surface that effectively locks the moisture in. But did you know that the pressure with which the pine tree draws up its water by the process of osmosis (called the osmotic pressure) is higher than that of an oak tree? This has the effect of lowering the freezing point, so that whereas the oak tree would already be forming ice crystals in its sap (obviously harmful, therefore eliminate the leaves to prevent osmosis), the pine, at the same temperature, because of the increased pressure, will not form any ice crystals. Therefore, pine leaves, you can stay on! Who gave the pine all this knowledge — knowledge so advanced and complex that not even the human brain can fathom it all, but knowledge so vital that without it the tree could not have survived until now. Yet here they are, in their millions, living testimony to the wisdom of their Designer and Creator.

The Tools of the Trade

Someone once played a trick on the owner of a garage. He bought an old car and removed the engine. The car was then towed to the top of a road with a gentle slope, at the bottom of which was situated the garage in question. The tow rope was removed, the hand brake released, and the engineless car coasted gently down in front of the garage. The driver approached the proprietor, and told him that he was having trouble starting his car, and could he possibly have a look? With an air of confidence, the experienced mechanic sat in the car and turned the ignition key. No sound. Again — no sound. He pressed the hood lever and marched purposely to the front of the car to investigate. He lifted up the hood and peered inside. He stood up, scratched his head, blinked a couple of times, and peered again. There was nothing there! With a look of incredulity, he turned to the car's driver, and told him that he was not surprised that he was experiencing some difficulty in starting his car, since the car had no engine! The driver fought to keep a straight face, and registered surprise. The cogs and wheels inside the mechanic's head started turning rapidly, wondering how an engineless car had managed to drive into his garage in the first place — until eventually he realized that he was the victim of a practical joke.

The fact is that there will be some people who, when hearing this story, will not understand it. They will not know what the absence of an engine has to do with the inability of the car to move. That group of people can be wonderful in character, even high in intelligence, perhaps talented in many ways, but one thing is sure. They are impractical. Ask them to calculate the *molad* of the New Moon in 71 years' time, and you'll have the answer in a flash, but ask them to fix a curtain rod in your front room, and you'll be sorry you ever asked. Ask them the square root of your birthdate, and you'll have the answer before the question has left your lips, but ask them to fix a shelf in your kitchen, and the hammering and chiseling — not to mention the replastering — will make it cheaper to contemplate moving. Never allow an impractical person to mend your washing machine, plan your *chasunah*, or decorate your home. Just leave it to the specialists. They have the equipment, the know-how, and the practical sense to complete the job painlessly and quickly.

If specialized equipment is necessary to fix washing machines and change tires, you can imagine that it is even more vital if the task at hand is remaining alive. There are some remarkable examples of animals whose equipment is so specialized that it almost defies belief. How do you eat a melon? You probably take a knife and cut it into manageable slices, and then complete the operation with a spoon or a fork. Why

Swallowing an egg twice the width of its body
is the equivalent of you swallowing the refrigerator!

not just pop the complete melon into your mouth all at once? Is your mouth not sufficiently wide? Shame. Meet the African egg-eating snake whose diet consists of nothing but birds' eggs. It lives in trees, sleeps during the day, and searches for eggs at night. It is a very slim snake but is capable of swallowing eggs which are more than twice the width of its own body. (The equivalent of you swallowing the refrigerator.) The not-too-lovable snake stretches its elasticated jaws wide apart to fit around the egg, and its skin is especially flexible so that it does not burst as the egg moves down the line. Our little friend does not have many teeth (and those that it does have are blunt) so it won't break an egg by accident while swallowing it. But how will the snake break open the egg once it is inside it? The egg-eater has a row of 30 special 'teeth' that stick down from its backbone, in the form of spikes. Once it has swallowed an egg, the snake bends its head down, pushing the egg up against these spikes. This cuts a slit in the eggshell and the insides come gushing out. (Getting rid of the eggshell does not take long. The snake tightens its muscles to crush the shell, and then spits it out in a nice neat bundle. The whole egg-eating process takes about 15 minutes. Specialized equipment?)

Take a look (but not too close) at the friendly boa constrictor. It strikes its prey swiftly with its long, sharp teeth, which slope backwards into the mouth, so the more the victim struggles, the more firmly it is wedged on to them. Like so many snakes, the boa can swallow birds and other animals thicker than its own body because of its amazing jaw — the two halves move right apart at the hinge, and are joined only by muscle. (Just think how useful that would be next time you go to a *Kiddush* and find the choice of cream cakes just too good for words!) Think for a minute. This cursed animal can swallow a goat whole. That must take some time. How does it manage to breathe while its mouth is engaged? The answer is the same specialized equipment that divers use. The boa constrictor is equipped with a snorkel-like windpipe which allows it to breathe while swallowing its meal. Without a nose to provide an alternative inlet for air, we would never be able to breathe while our mouths were blocked. Each creature has been provided with the equipment that it requires.

While on the subject of snakes and other reptiles you would rather not know, how about the following? One poisonous snake, the viper, has specially designed fangs that act as hypodermic syringes with which to inject the poison into its victim. These fangs are so long that, when they are not being used, they hinge back against the roof of its mouth. Why don't you learn to hinge your teeth back when not in use? It could be useful if you don't want to smile at someone!

For that matter, why has the walrus, which has enormously long tusks, not managed to acquire a convenient hinge? The answer is that you receive the tools that you require. The spitting cobra, on the other hand, does not inject its poison, it just squirts a fine stream of venom at its enemy's face, aiming for the eyes. Surely to squirt, you need special equipment? It has it. The venom is squeezed out through holes at the tip of the fangs. It can spit about six times before the venom supply runs out, but do not worry, this can be replaced within a day. Bear in mind that any animal or reptile possessing a poison-attacking capability must also be equipped with a built-in immunity to its own poison, a pumping mechanism (connected to the nervous system), and the reservoir to hold the poison. And each part of the equipment must have worked perfectly from the very beginning to avoid the animal either committing suicide, or being eaten for the sake of its orange-juice content which it was still trying so hard to convert to nerve-paralyzing poison.

And what would you say about the baby snakes that get out of their eggs all by themselves, with their special little egg teeth with which they saw through the shell? Then perhaps they need time to develop their unpleasant skills? Really! Little cobras can bite and kill as soon as they hatch from their eggs, and just one tablespoon of their dried poison could kill over 160,000 mice! Specialized equipment? Who taught them?

Can we change the subject? How do you manage to keep warm in the winter? Sit shivering next to the radiator? Cocoon yourself with layer upon layer of clothing? It s a shame that you are not a reindeer. This animal is both tough and enduring. Its coat is waterproof and cold does not bother it. Not surprising! Its fur is made of millions of hollow hairs, which trap the air and warm it, and gives the reindeer remarkable buoyancy. Not for nothing do Eskimos wear reindeer fur, for a jacket of reindeer fur is a fair equivalent of a life belt. Just think for a moment. How do you make your hair hollow? Reindeers live in the barren wastelands of the north, and being large animals, require many pounds of vegetation each day in order to survive. In the white wilderness of snow, how can they find their desperately needed food? Nothing is a problem when you have the proper equipment. Their split hooves have a specially designed sharp edge which can cut through all but the hardest of ice. Can you imagine a farmer growing a hoe out of one toe, and perhaps a plow from the other? Well, why not? And how about coal miners growing an electric lamp out of their foreheads — now that would be useful! Sorry, you either have the equipment or you don't.

While on the subject of cold, come and have a look at the polar bear. He is either swimming in the freezing polar waters, or stalking the frosty ice floes. But he is never cold. His special equipment includes air spaces in his fur, oil glands in his skin, and a thick layer of fat. The list does not end there. His toes are partially webbed, and he has hair on the bottom of his feet, suiting them perfectly well for both swimming and walking on the slippery ice. Have you seen photographs of Arctic Circle explorers? You will have noticed that they all wear sunglasses to protect themselves against ice glare and snow blindness. So how does the polar bear manage? Not really a problem, when you have been equipped with special arctic sunglasses, in the form of a membranous third eyelid! Do you need a special tool for hooking seals out of their air holes in the ice? He has them. Unretractable claws, cat sharp, are precision instruments, perfect for the job, as is his extremely sensitive sense of smell. He can detect the scent of seal blubber at a distance of 20 miles. And we think that we have a keen sense of smell if we open the front door and know how good the *cholent* is going to be that Shabbos!

When the mechanic comes to repair our washing machine carrying his bag of tools, we happily acknowledge the design of each one. Every animal comes carrying the tools for its individual trade. May we happily acknowledge the great Intelligence that designed it all?

The Blink of an Eyelid

You can only truly appreciate something new when you have had to endure the outdated version. A young man needed to buy a car. Having limited money and even more limited expertise, he naively bought a used car from a stranger who was only too delighted to sell the unsuspecting man a mechanized garbage can, assuring him of its phenomenal prowess in the most superlative of terms. The gullible guy gave the *gelt,* and happily drove home. It was then that he noticed the first fault. The car did not seem to have too much suspension. The body seemed a little too close to the ground, and even riding over a matchstick jarred the car to its last bolt. He comforted himself by thinking that racing cars also have low suspension, and this car must be a racing model. Talk about wishful thinking! The second fault — a certain weakness in the rear axle — was slightly more serious, and he noticed it soon enough. As he was rounding a curve in the road, he suddenly heard a horrible grinding sound. Pulling over to the side, he saw to his horror that the two rear wheels were slanting diagonally in an inward direction. The back axle had snapped. There is nothing like learning the hard way!

Being much wiser now, and still needing a car, he went to another car dealer. They settled on a much newer model than the previous tin can on wheels. Before completing the deal, the young man asked the dealer, "Does the suspension work, and is the rear axle strong?" The dealer gave him a pitying look and said, "You've had a bad experience, so you ask. But when you buy a decent car, such as the one you are about to purchase, you don't have to ask whether the suspension is in order, or if the rear axle is strong!" He was right, but you can understand the customer. You can be sure that he appreciated the suspension in his new car, and blessed the rear axle, and probably the front one, too, for remaining intact.

Imagine that you were the proud owner of a new car. You were delighted that everything worked wonderfully, until you needed to clean the windshield. The windshield washer emitted no water, and the irregular blades just smeared the film of mud evenly across the windshield, obscuring your vision in a most efficient matter. Nowadays that is not a major problem. Make a quick visit to a garage, fill up the reservoir with water and a can of antifreeze, fit two new rubber blades on the wipers, and life is perfect once again. There is no doubt that you will appreciate the cleanliness and efficiency of your windshield-cleansing apparatus much more than anyone else. You appreciate perfection when you have experienced imperfection.

Do you have to be a car owner to appreciate windshield wipers and washers? The answer is that every single human being has been blessed with a pair of windshield wipers, windshield washers, incorporated into an integral plumbing system whose efficiency and technology far surpasses any car yet produced, and any that is likely to be produced in the future. Look someone in the eye, and you can see them for yourself — your very own eyelids.

May I ask you some questions? If you are a car driver, what is one of the most uncomfortable, if not one of the most dangerous, events that can happen while driving? It must surely be the mundane activity of sneezing. Imagine driving in the fast lane, in the pouring rain, passing a heavy truck that is splashing gallons of spray. You need every ounce of concentration to keep your distance from the truck and the side of the road in poor visibility conditions. Suddenly you feel an irrepressible urge to sneeze. The problem is that it is impossible to sneeze with your eyes open. Try it! For those couple of seconds that you are busy sneezing, you are literally driving with your eyes closed! It's frightening.

Why does this terrible feeling of panic not take place every time you blink? Isn't your vision also impaired during blinking? The fact is that no activity is impaired by the action of blinking, no matter how critical the activity and how great the concentration required. How is that? Did you in your childhood ever play at staring? The object of the game is for two people to sit across a table, open their eyes wide, and stare into each other's eyes. The loser is the one who blinks first. There is a limit to the length of time that you can keep your eyes open without blinking. Why? Why do you have to blink? Do you have to think to blink? If blinking needs no thinking, how do you know when to do it? Who gives the order? What mechanism puts the blink into motion? Do you blink in your sleep? Why do you blink if you see a fly or a fist flying in your direction?

Now for some answers. Just as the car has electrical circuitry, we have a nervous system. The nervous system is composed of bundles of nerve cells, specially designed to carry tiny electrical messages. The body's control center is the brain. Part of the nervous system is voluntary, which means it's under your conscious control; and part is automatic, which means that it controls itself. Let us imagine that you are sitting on a chair, reading a book, while eating an apple. Here come the voluntary actions. When you read, your eyes scan back and forth, and your brain interprets the image patterns that your eyes see. When you eat, your jaw muscles make your teeth chew, and your tongue moves the food around in your mouth. As you sit, you may not be aware of your body posture, but you constantly keep your balance and you regularly change position to rest muscles. Now for the automatic ones. As food reaches the back of your throat and you swallow, automatic muscle movement takes over. When you digest, your stomach mashes the apple you have eaten and muscles in your intestinal wall push it along. At the same time, muscles in the walls of the arteries make them wider or narrower to direct blood where it is needed. Some actions are part voluntary and part involuntary. (Breathing — you can control your rate of breathing, but you cannot consciously stop breathing. Blinking — you can blink faster or slower, but you cannot consciously cease blinking.) A reflex action is an automatic reaction that happens incredibly fast, before you even have time to think about it. A reflex occurs by itself, even if your attention is elsewhere. Babies cannot control many of their movements, and they cannot feed or clean themselves. But they are far from helpless, and they do many things automatically. The 'Moro' reflex, for example, occurs if the baby suddenly falls back or is startled. The baby throws out its arms and legs, as if to catch hold of something. The rooting reflex helps feeding. If touched on the cheek, the baby turns to that side and moves its mouth to find the source of food.

Clap your hands loudly in front of a friend's face (with permission!) and see how your friend blinks immediately. That is a reflex action to protect his precious twin cameras. If an object comes towards your head, you will respond with a series of actions, almost without thinking. Your eyelids come together to close your eyes, and facial muscles contract to tense and toughen your skin. Your head jerks sideways and backwards so that your face is out of line. Your shoulder and arm muscles lift your arms and hands in front of your face as a shield. All that is done without thinking. It is pro-grammed into your brain, like a disk in a computer.

The real wonder is your eyelids. The next time you step into your car, take a look at the windshield wipers, their shape, their construction, their function, and see if you can discern design. Now look at your very own eyelids. Produced from car-tilage and skin, containing muscles and nerves, apart from the spiky fence of eyelashes at their leading edge, they drop down in a perfect fit to cover the eyes (to provide curtains to eliminate light, to act as a shutter to provide protection, and to bathe and lubricate the eyes with a wonder fluid) in a frac-tion of a second. The muscular action which controls blinking is so efficient, so well coordinated, that the amount of time the eyelids actually cover the pupil (the aperture through which light passes) is so infinitesimal that it barely registers in the brain, and does not disturb the sense of sight at all.

The surface of the eye must be kept moist, otherwise the exposed parts of the cornea and conjunctiva (the front surface of the eye) dry up and can be damaged. For that reason we have been created with a fountain producing tears, a fantas-tic liquid containing sodium chloride and sodium bicarbonate, not to mentions lysozyme, an enzyme that destroys bacteria, strategically situated just above the eyeball. It's great — you never have to fill the reservoir, you never have to add anti-freeze for the winter, and you never have to replace the wiper blades. And you think that your new car is the last word in technology! The brain has a standing order to command the eyelids to blink, thereby distributing the wonder fluid over the eye's surface every few seconds. If you want, try not to blink; you will not succeed. The brain has its orders. If you blink once every five seconds, that is 12,960 times in a full day (you do not blink while you sleep!). Each blink is a blessing, each eyelid is a miracle of design, and each blessing takes place almost without your being aware of it. The Creator cre-ated the machinery to produce nearly 13,000 wonders each day, each wonder as fast as the blink of an eyelid. The Creator can deliver our redemption, which will also come as fast as a blink of an eyelid. Let us experience it, and let it be soon!

Highway Patrol

Things are not what they used to be. Once upon a time it was possible to sail down an empty highway early on a Sunday morning, with nothing in sight except a stray crow, and not be overly concerned about the speed limit. There was a good chance that all the highway patrolmen were fast asleep, and should you chance upon a passing police car, you could immediately adjust your speed. No longer. We now live in the age of cameras that stand silent vigil by the roadside, connected electronically to Police Headquarters, where the speed of the passing vehicle, and, even worse, its registration number, are entered into the all-powerful computer. Should an errant car exceed the speed limit, all evidence has been recorded, and you will be notified by letter, no doubt written by the very same obnoxious computer.

One shouldn't complain. As far as policing is concerned, the good old days were certainly far from good. The police of old would patrol on foot, armed with a wooden stick and a whistle. What would they do if they were confronted with a criminal who was not particularly frightened by a stick? What would they do if they had to blow their trusty whistle to summon help, and no one could hear them? Worse still, what would happen if the little ball inside the whistle (I have never yet discovered the function of the little ball inside a whistle!) had been consumed by some hungry ants? What would our brave policeman do then? Problem. Indeed the picture of an irate and overweight red-faced policeman panting as he pursues escaping criminals, he on his heavy police bike, waving his nightstick with one hand, trying to steer his bike and keep his helmet on with the other; while the laughing criminals wave to their adversary from the back of their sleek getaway car, remains the comical caricature that many have of policing methods of days gone by.

Things have certainly changed. Aided by police helicopters and the most advanced computer technology, with an approach which is both confident and professional, police forces throughout the world have never been better equipped to apprehend criminals and maintain law and order. Theoretically at least, our cities should be safer than ever, our homes more secure. In a fast-advancing civilization, policing must keep pace or else admit defeat. Would you like to come to a place where the police force is so sophisticated, so clever and so effective, that even the most advanced methods of our uniformed friends would resemble the Keystone Kops by comparison? Do you accept the invitation? Then come and have a close look at yourself.

The story that you will hear is one of heroism and bravery, for inside the body are a stalwart band of cells whose task is to constantly battle against all kinds of invading germs.

Every day, every minute and every second they battle, keeping you fit and healthy. Would you believe that every single day, 1,000 million defender cells are manufactured in your bone marrow? Among those defender cells are the following fighting soldiers: Enter the *neutrophil*. This cell is full of chemicals, the type of chemicals that destroy germs. They travel around the bloodstream armed and ready to destroy any invaders. (You understand, I'm sure, that to enter your body was no simple matter for this, or any germ, for sentries and security devices have been provided to protect you. Your skin, protected with a layer of dead skin-cells, and slightly acidic in content, provides an effective barrier, efficiently vanquishing many of the germs that land. Saliva in the mouth contains a powerful antiseptic that successfully eliminates many of the germs that come into your mouth with the food.) When a neutrophil detects an invading germ, it actually consumes it and kills it with its deadly chemicals. This destroys the germ, but unfortunately the neutrophil is sometimes destroyed in the process. There are plenty more, however, to carry on the good work.

Another vital member of the police force is a large cell called the *macrophage*. This is the scavenger of the system, constantly scouring the territories of our bodies, alert to anything that seems out of place. It patrols the bloodstream, and settles down in many parts of the body. There are millions in the lungs, for example, continually eating up the dust and germs that you breathe in every day. Like their cousins the neutrophils, they are full of germ-destroying chemicals. The macrophage, however, does not self-destruct, and lives much longer. As it fights its brave fight against the invading germ, the macrophage does something magnificent. It plucks a special piece (called an *antigen*) from the invader, and displays it on its own cell surface like a captured banner of war. This flag plays a critical role in the immune system, since it alerts specialized cells — called *lymphocytes* — that there is trouble afoot, and they come to join the battle.

These lymphocytes are the cleverest of all the defender cells. They don't all attack every germ they meet; instead, different squads of lymphocytes attack different germs. The captured flag of a germ was recognized by one of the lymphocytes by its shape. (Amazingly, these squads of lymphocytes, each programmed to recognize and fight a different antigen, were formed in your body even before you were born.) The lymphocyte cells that first recognized the enemy antigens carry no weapons (rather like British policemen). Instead, they send urgent chemical signals to a small squadron of allies — the killer cells who are trained to recognize and destroy the enemy. Their message: Multiply fast! (Next time you want to think of something amazing, ask yourself how you would contact one of your friends chemically. Not only is it necessary for the message to arrive at the correct address, but the message must be comprehensible. It's no use sending your friend some hydrochloric acid which you know means "Come to the chasunah at 8:00 p.m.," if your friend thinks that hydrochloric acid means "You're only invited for the dancing and *sheva brachos* at 10:30 p.m." What we consider strange and unusual, our defender cells are doing all the time.) The message is received, and soon the commando cells of the lymphocyte army multiply quickly. Some cells in the lymphocyte army release special weapons, called antibodies. By sticking to the surface of unwelcome invaders, antibody molecules damage them, making them easier targets for the mobile rubbish-disposal units, the macrophages. Antibodies can be even more potent. As they lock on to the enemy's antigens, the antibodies attract substances in the bloodstream which, when combined, detonate like a bomb, blasting through the invader's cell membrane.

As more antibodies are produced (at peak performance, the commando cells can produce thousands of antibodies per second), the tide turns, and the struggle is won. The lymphocyte squad is stronger than ever, with one important difference. The victory has not been forgotten. Some of the lymphocytes become memory lymphocytes, and remain on alert within the body for years. If the same germ tries to invade again, the lymphocyte squad is much stronger, and the battle won more easily. This explains why most children experience only one attack of measles or mumps. The secret of immunization is to create harmless dummy germs in the laboratory (microbes that have been weakened sufficiently to lose their power to cause disease, but strong enough to retain the power to confer immunity) and introduce them into the body. As they enter, a lymphocyte squad is immediately alerted. This quickly multiplies into a strong army that attacks the dummy germs. Now, if the real germs ever attack after you have been vaccinated, you already possess an army of lymphocytes to protect you.

Have you ever seen policemen helping people in distress? Don't be surprised, for your very own policemen are equally adept. Defender cells do not just work together to fight illnesses, they also help mend your body if it is damaged. Imagine that you have cut your finger. It bleeds because you have cut through some skin cells. The blood soon becomes dark and sticky, and stops flowing, forming a blood clot. (Not as simple as it sounds! When body tissues are damaged, they trigger off a series of reactions in the blood. First, chemicals are released by platelets in the blood. Then, these chemicals convert a protein called *fibrinogen* into microscopic threads of *fibrin.* These form a sticky mesh that traps the blood cells, and in this way the clot builds up.) If harmful bacteria enter the cut, they must be destroyed. Chemical messages released by injured cells alert neutrophils and lymphocytes. They leave the bloodstream by the thousands and move into the blood clot, hunting for germs. After 24 hours, the macrophages start to move in. They begin work, cleaning up dead cells, live bacteria and clotted blood. After about three days, your defender cells have cleaned up the cut in a most efficient manner, and all danger of infection is past. Slowly the defender cells and builder cells disappear; they have done their job. Now the skin cells take over, growing out from the edge of the cut.

It is absolutely amazing. Silent, fearless, and superbly capable, there is no police force in the world as efficient and as well planned as the one in your very own body. Something to be grateful for!

מִבְּשָׂרִי אֶחֱזֶה אֱלוֹקַ!
From my flesh I behold G-d!

Navigator Extraordinary

There are some words in Yiddish which defy translation. One of them is *shlemiel*. (Another is *shlemazel*, and the only way to explain the difference in meaning is by means of illustration: A *shlemiel* spills the soup on the *shlemazel's* pants.) Even if you cannot translate the word *shlemiel*, you will surely recognize him when you meet him. In summer camp, he is the nightmare of every head counselor. One day, the head counselor decides that the campers are going on a hike. The children are taken by bus to some out-of-the-way location, and split into groups. Each counselor is equipped with a map, compass, and strict instructions as to when to return to the bus. The law of averages will tell you that if you send out 10 groups, one group is bound to come back late. The head counselor is annoyed and frustrated. He made it absolutely clear that everyone was to return on time. Was the group lost? Should they wait? Are they in trouble? Sure enough, just before the state troopers are summoned, the celebrated group straggles in, blissfully unaware of the turmoil that they have caused. When the irate head counselor tackles the counselor in charge, he replies ingenuously, "I couldn't read the map; I was sure that north was this way; I thought the compass was a clock; I wasn't sure which way to hold the map." That counselor would qualify for the title *shlemiel.*

It is a bit unfair. There are some people who just have a very poor sense of direction. Place them in an unfamiliar street, even minutes from their home, and they might as well be in North Korea. A young man from America recently arrived in England to learn in a *yeshivah.* After being greeted, he was asked which town he was from. The answer was Monsey. He was then asked if Monsey is to the north or south of New York. A look of complete bewilderment spread over his face. "I don't know," he said, "it's in the country!" Don't blame him — if you have never seen a map, then how should you know where anything is in relation to anything else?

How indeed? Have you ever traveled by plane, looked out the window, seen an expanse of featureless sea beneath you and wondered where you were? How on earth should you know? You only hope that up front, in the pilot's cabin, the navigator is not looking out his window and asking the same question! Everyone understands that without the most sophisticated navigational aids and instruments it is impossible to travel accurately over long distances. What, therefore, would you say about the possibility of traveling from Alaska (at the northwesterly tip of Canada, just across the Bering Strait from Russia) to a small island in the Pacific Ocean called Hawaii? The journey is over anonymous ocean, and there are no islands in midroute for stopping off (to ask the way) or to rest. How would you like to undertake the trip,

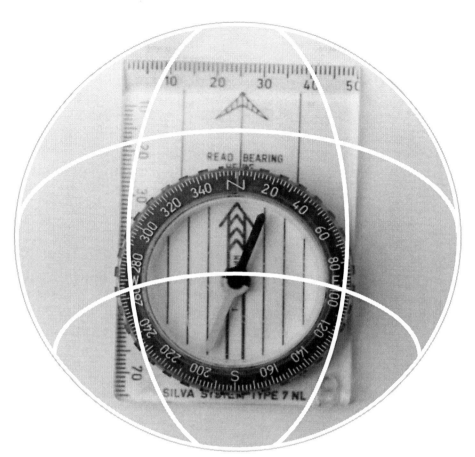

The golder plover flies for 2,500 miles over open sea, and arrives safely at its destination, without a compass. How?

with no map or compass, no sextant or chart to assist you? Impossible? Perhaps for a human, but not for a bird. Bear in mind that birds have very small brains compared to humans (the term 'birdbrain,' when applied to humans, is not a compliment). Their ability to learn is severely limited. They are born, however, with instincts which are so complex that to this very day they defy comprehension.

Consider, for example, the winter vacation of the golden plover. This bird lives in Alaska during the summer months. When the winter approaches, it sets off on its epic voyage to Hawaii. This involves a nonstop flight which takes it across the open sea, where no island punctuates the watery expanse. In addition, the bird cannot swim, so that a stop for a rest is impossible. The flight is a distance of at least 2,500 miles (depending on its starting-off point), lasts 88 hours, and involves no less than a quarter of a million consecutive wing beats. Now everyone knows that one of the chief limiting factors for nonstop air travel by plane is the difficulty in carrying sufficient fuel. How then does the golden plover carry sufficient fuel to burn enough energy to enable it to fly for 88 hours nonstop? Think also about the following. To ensure the necessary flying capacity, the bird must be of as light a build as possible, and excess weight must be avoided at all costs. (Think of the stringent rules employed by airlines — especially those traveling to *Eretz Yisrael* — to reduce overweight.) Likewise, use of fuel has to be as economical as possible. The first step is to choose the most economical cruising speed. Should the bird fly too slowly, it would consume too much fuel simply to stay airborne. If it flies too quickly, it wastes too much energy overcoming wind resistance. If the bird knew about these facts, it would be able to fly as efficiently as possible! The fact is that each bird has an optimum speed, depending on the aerodynamic construction of its fuselage and wings. It is a known fact that birds gear themselves exactly to this energy-saving speed. Who provided them with the information?

Consider some further amazing details. The bird's starting weight is 7 ounces, of which 2½ ounces are stored as layers of fat to be used as fuel. It is known that the golden plover converts 0.6 percent per hour of its current body weight into energy and heat. If you calculate this over a period of 88 hours, you will find that the golden plover has used almost 3 ounces of fuel. This is definitely more than the available 2½ ounces! Bear in mind that the bird cannot go below the limit of 4½ ounces. Thus, in spite of flying at the speed which minimizes his fuel consumption, the bird does not have enough fuel to reach Hawaii. Why does it not crash into the sea a good 500 miles before it reaches its destination, when it should have run out of fuel? The answer is breathtaking. The same Designer Who gave the bird its aerodynamic shape gave the bird a vital piece of information: not to fly singly, but in V-formation. In V-formation it saves 23 percent of its energy, enough to reach its winter quarters safely. But that is not all. The extra power saved by flying in this manner will leave the golden plover with ¼ ounce of fat in reserve after 88 hours of flying. Do not for one moment think that this extra fuel is superfluous. It has been included so that the bird reaches its destination even against a contrary wind. The extent of intelligence is breathtaking.

Now consider the following questions. How does the bird know how much fat is necessary for fuel? How does it arrange to have precisely this amount on board before embarking on its momentous journey? How does the bird know the distance and the specific rate of fuel consumption? Even more incredibly, how does the bird know where to go — the first time it travels, it has never been there before! And the most perplexing question of all: How does the bird know the way? The bird's navigational achievement is unparalleled in any human activity. You have to bear in mind that the golden plover must continually alter course to allow for winds which drift it off target. Even a slight diversion off course while crossing the endless, featureless expanse of the ocean would be fatal for migrating land birds. Keeping on course cannot be a matter of trial and error. Without navigational methods, the birds would never reach their destination, and no species could survive such an overwhelming attrition rate. To suggest that they follow their parents is simply inaccurate. Many species fly solo, following no one (see Chapter 8 — Matter of Instinct).

Birds' capabilities extend beyond the bounds of our imagination. They can determine their homeward course over enormous distances even when all possible aids to orientation have been removed on the outward journey. On one occasion, a manx shearwater (*peffinus puffinus!*) was taken from its nest in Wales to Boston, in the U.S.A. It arrived back in its nest in 12 days, 12 hours and 31 minutes, after a 3,100-mile nonstop transatlantic flight. Experiments in which birds were anaesthetized for the outward journey, or their cages were made to rotate constantly, made no difference whatsoever. When birds migrate over wide, windswept oceans, they are bound to drift. This drift must be continuously compensated for in a feedback system, in order to avoid losing energy by flying a longer route. The birds are equipped with an autopilot which constantly measures its geographical position, comparing the data with its individually 'programmed' destination, ensuring an economical, direct and energy-saving flight. This would sound fine if you were talking about a jumbo jet, but we are talking about a smidgen of a bird that has never ever been to the destination where it is heading with such unnerving accuracy, has not received any lessons in navigation, and possesses a brain not much larger than a pea. That it possess fantastic navigational skills is beyond doubt. It is just the question of precisely where in the bird this vital skill is housed, and the precise mechanics of the amazing system that no one (except the Designer) understands.

When John Alcock and Arthur Brown flew from Newfoundland to Ireland on June 4th, 1919 — the first nonstop transatlantic flight — they became instant heroes. Their remarkable achievement was recognized and praised throughout the world (they were both knighted five days after they landed), all the more so because they ended their historic flight only 10 miles off course. They had a compass, charts, air speed indicator, drift indicator, a clock and a sextant to assist in their historic journey. The golden plover, together with millions of birds, does the same, and so much more, year in and year out. May we, who look for and recognize a Creator, record our particular praise for this fantastic achievement?

ou can tell me that the first mechanical cash register was invented by Hyman McAddem in New York City in the year 1876. You might be right and you might be wrong. It doesn't matter, because 80 years later, our local Jewish delicatessen owner was still blissfully unaware of it. He stood behind the counter with a permanently worried look. His wife also worked in the shop, and she was a strong personality (part of the fun of shopping was to listen to them arguing) — two very good reasons to explain his look of constant worry. He wore a long white apron, which was always stained with the vinegar of the schmalz herring barrel, and his badge of honor was the pencil behind his ear. It was never long (it seems that in those days you could purchase half-pencils). As he collected each item requested from the many shelves (the store was definitely not self-service), he would whip out his stub of pencil and scrawl a figure in thick lettering on the back of the brown paper bag. At the end of your shopping spree, he drew a line under the bottom figure, and added up the total. It was a pleasure to watch him. It never took him more than five seconds, and he was never wrong. The brown bag was your receipt, you could check it, but he was infallible. What a brain!

Go now to your supermarket and you will see how the brown paper bag has developed. Every item in your shopping cart, from the prepackaged bag of oranges to the box of sugar, is bar-coded. The highly trained assistant sits at her stool and absent-mindedly passes each purchase in front of a glass screen which, with the aid of a laser beam, 'reads' the bar code, sends the appropriate information to the computer, which programs the printer to print the amount on the cash register receipt. A high degree of training is necessary to learn how to hold the purchase the right way up in front of the scanner! After completion of the transaction, the total is displayed on the screen, and you pay. The screen then informs the assistant how much change to give, and you are free to go. Not a single word needs to be spoken by anyone (are you surprised that so many people suffer from loneliness?), the computer-laser-scanner-checkout has done it all. What an electronic brain!

Which do you think is more efficient? Be prepared for some surprises, for in between your ears is assembled a piece of equipment whose complexity is barely understood, and which almost defies description. In looks, it is humble. It resembles a grey custard, and weighs as much as a large grapefruit, but never ever judge something by looks alone! Compared to the brain, other wonders of the universe pale into insignificance. Your brain is responsible for your intelligence, creativity, memories, perceptions, reactions and emotions. Some of its

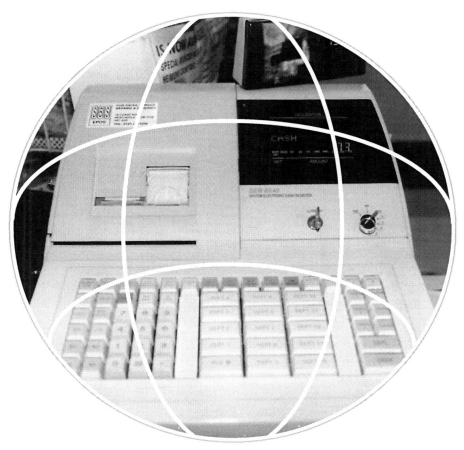

A big advance over the brown paper bag — but primitive compared to your brain

processes you are aware of, such as thought and memory, or working out a complex piece of *Gemara*. However, your brain does much more without your realizing it. It controls your body functions, such as the heartbeat, breathing, and digestion. It monitors the concentrations of substances (glucose and carbon dioxide) in the blood, adjusts water and nutrient levels, and brings on feelings of hunger and thirst when supplies of food or fluid run low. Your brain also screens the gigantic amounts of information that are gathered continuously by your senses. Why are you not overwhelmed by all the information? The brain selects what is important, and ignores the rest. If you are reading, and in the background you hear someone call you, the brain is capable of tuning one out! The brain is capable of shifting gears instantly. If you slip on the ice, your brain immediately directs you to regain your balance, and then signals your arm to break the fall. Finally, if you hit the ground, your brain will inform you of the pain. And the event is stored in your memory to warn you to walk carefully on ice in the future.

Enter a huge library and gaze at the rows of shelves containing thousands of volumes reaching to the ceiling. Your little brain contains all that information, and much more. Not only that, but every piece of information can be instantly recalled. If I ask you if you have ever heard of someone called Vasso Epthymayou, the answer would be a clear yes or no. You wouldn't ask me to come back in a couple of days, or say that you will have to look it up; you know, instantly. If you hear a piece of music, and someone asks you if you have heard it before, you know instantly whether you have or not. There is no doubt! If your answer is in the negative, and the questioner insists that the piece is famous, and that you should know it, you in turn will insist that it can be as famous as it likes, you know for sure that you have not heard it! How much information has your brain sifted through to arrive at that definitive conclusion — and how long did it take?

Our brain is so chemically active that although it weighs only one-fiftieth of the weight of the body, it uses up to one-fifth of the body's energy supply. (Reduce it just a little, perhaps after a heavy meal, where the blood supply is diverted to the stomach to help digest the great load, and you will not be surprised that the brain is not at its most active, and you feel drowsy.) Let there be a more severe shortage, and you faint. The brain demands a steady supply of nourishment, and in situations of starvation, it receives the first call on any available supply.

If you knew the entire *Shas*, and someone who was not too well educated praised you for being able to learn a *Mishnah*, the compliment would ring hollow. Similarly, some people, wishing to praise the design of the brain, compare it to a computer. What an insult! No computer exists that can duplicate all of the brain's myriad functions. Just take the component parts. Under your size 7 hat you have some 30 billion nerve cells, called *neurons*. It would be relatively easy to comprehend if the neurons were connected to the brain like the spokes of a wheel, but they are not. Most of these neurons are connected to a great many other neurons; one estimate is that, on average, each neuron is cross-connected with between 10,000 and 100,000 others. This means a total of 10 trillion connections. A complete wiring diagram of this network would stagger the imagination. All of the telephone cables of the world would comprise no more than a small fraction of it all. A neuron looks something like a spider attached to a filament. The spider is the cell body, the filament is the nerve wire (the axon) and the legs are the dendrites of the cell. The legs pick up a signal from adjacent neurons, pass it to the body, the signal is in turn passed along by the filament at speeds up to 225 mph. After each signal passes, it takes the filament about $1/2000$ of a second to chemically recharge itself. At no point do any of the neurons touch each other. Instead signals are passed like sparks over a gap. At each 'firing,' one nerve chemically communicates with another. That means that each signal that travels to or from the brain is in fact a series of millions of separate chemical reactions, whizzing along at 330 feet per second. Be honest. Do you now completely understand how the brain receives and sends messages? And you want to compare the brain to a computer? Don't insult the brain!

If you want to know the speed that your brain reacts to external stimuli, think of the following. When a top-ranked tennis player hits a mighty serve, the ball travels at more than 100 mph. The opponent has less than a third of a second to note the speed and direction of the ball, move into position, watch for the bounce and spin, and swing the racket for the return shot. Such sports might mean much money, but lives do not depend on the outcome. What about motor racing? At 200 mph, a racing car travels almost 330 feet per second. The driver's safety depends on reactions measured in hundredths of a second. Everyone admits to the fantastic design of the racing car that achieves such superlative performance. Everyone praises the racing driver for his lightning reflexes. Will everyone please praise the Creator of the brain that was able to design a racing car, together with the Creator of the brain that can perform with such speed and dexterity?

No one carries eggs home in their pockets. Specially designed containers (plastic or styrofoam) perform their protective job well. Similarly, the brain resides inside a well-protected fortress. The skull is ¼ inch thick at the top, and even thicker at the base. It is bathed in a watery fluid that cushions it from shock. An effective barrier (made from blood) acts as a gatekeeper. It welcomes the vital glucose fuel, but blocks out bacteria and toxic substances.

So you think that the laser-beam computer-linked electronic cash register is an impressive piece of technology — more effective than the brown bag? How do you know? Have you seen one at your supermarket? What does that mean? It means that at some stage you focused your eyes (working in unison) on the machine in question, and watched it operate. As you gazed at it, you comprehended what it was and understood its function. You formed an opinion about it, and perhaps communicated that opinion to others, either by speech, or in writing. Whichever it was, that opinion and your mental image of it remained in your memory long enough to recall it and discuss it. Is your glance, observation, comprehension and memory any different from the very machine under discussion? Are you impressed by the cash register? Are you impressed by the mind? If so, think — and thank!

Holland is the Netherlands, and Netherlands means low country. It is indeed a low country, and extremely flat. It is surprising that there is a Dutch word — *heuvel* — for hill, because there are so few hills in Holland. Much of the country is below sea level, and large areas of land, especially in the northwest of the country, have been reclaimed from the sea. All this will explain the great importance of the dikes. Dikes are artificial embankments built to keep out the sea, and should they ever be breached, the sea would pour into the land so laboriously snatched from the watery depths. You might have heard that recently, the country faced its most perilous threat since the war. Very heavy rain had swollen the Maas and Waal rivers — which flow through the country from east to west — to unprecedented levels. Because the rivers are above sea level, and so much of the land is beneath sea level, these rivers are also held in check by the dikes. As the rain continued, the river levels rose ever higher, and the pressure on the dikes increased daily. They could either be breached from above, or weakened from below. Either way, the country was threatened with calamity, and one quarter of a million Dutchmen were evacuated from their towns and villages. Military personnel were rushed to the dikes to reinforce and strengthen the most threatened areas. Everyone was watching those dikes, for all understood the terrible danger. Were even one dike to be breached, the floodgates would have swept open — immersing large areas of Holland in a murky flood. The story had a happy ending, for just inches away from disaster, the rains eased and the river levels slowly subsided. Phew!

Could you imagine, in a fairy-tale situation perhaps, that someone, a great hero, would have injected the raging waters with a substance that would cause the water to coagulate, thicken, and stop the instant that the dike was breached? Wouldn't that be something? Naturally, this miraculous substance would have to be ineffective while the dikes were intact, otherwise the river would solidify, and the fish would be most unhappy! It is asking a lot, it is true, but this super-substance must only begin its flood-saving work if the restraining dike were broken, and at no other time. If someone could only invent such a substance, he would be a national hero. No more threat of flooding — no more danger — he would have safeguarded the life and prosperity of the land. Bravo!

Sometimes, everyday facts are more wonderful than fairy-tales. Within our bodies flows a waterway which covers more miles than a global airline. We are talking about the liquid of life, our bloodstream. This bloodstream, very much like a busy river, has many roles. Blood carries life-giving oxygen to all body parts (it only has 100 trillion stopping-off places, the number of cells in your body), and at the same time collects carbon dioxide for removal by the lungs. It is the highway for distributing vitamins and nutrients, while at the same time it picks up wastes for removal by the kidneys. It is the river-way that carries white blood cells that fight germs, and at the same time it carries hormones, those vital chemical messengers that stimulate and coordinate body processes. It evens out the temperature in different parts of the body by taking heat from the busy parts, such as the heart and active muscles, to warm the less active, cooler parts and the far-flung extremities. It flows for an incredible 75,000 miles of route (remember that it has 100 trillion stations), and it flows under pressure. The pressure is the result of the action of the main pump — the heart — to force the blood in surges around the huge area that it has to travel. The mighty river flows, and is held in check by the dikes, called the skin. That skin barrier is a mere 5 mm. (¼ of an inch) thick, and is the only barrier between the body's interior, with its delicate cells and finely balanced fluids, and the harsh, changing conditions of the outside world. If that dike is breached at any point, the blood, under pressure, should come pouring through unchecked and unstoppable. The danger threatening Holland should be a danger to everyone! But this is where the fairy-tale comes true.

We know from our own selves of the miracle that takes place whenever we sustain an injury. A sharp pin pricks into the skin and punctures a small blood vessel just under the surface. Blood, under pressure from inside the body, oozes from the cut. What happens next is the miracle which should make us jump in the air with happiness! There is a substance in the fluid which makes it coagulate and self-seal! How does it happen?

Imagine that you have a test tube full of blood, and you have divided the blood into its constituent parts. Fifty percent is composed of the lightest, watery portion of blood, called plasma. The heaviest portion is the red blood cells, and they constitute almost 45 percent. (There are about five million red cells in a pinhead-size drop of blood.) Finally there are the white blood cells and platelets, which make up less than one percent of the blood. In the same pinhead of blood you will find 10,000 white cells and 250,000 platelets. When the skin is punctured, platelets (produced in the bone marrow) rush to the scene. When they meet the open air, they become sticky, and clump together at the scene of the wound. That is a great kindness, because their presence is vitally required. What for? Dissolved within the plasma is a protein, called *fibrinogen.* The platelets release chemicals which react with the fibrinogen and turn it into *fibrin.* The fibrin appears out of the solution as tiny microscopic threads, which form a sticky mesh that actually traps the red blood cells, together with even more platelets, forming what is called a young clot. This clot has created an effective plug which stops any additional blood from leaking out, and equally important, prevents the entry of bacteria and poisons.

In order to fully (or even partially) understand the wonder of the clotting process, it is necessary to know a little more, and to ask a vital question. If the blood contains clotting agents, which can successfully seal a puncture and repair the skin completely, why does this clotting agent not clot the blood within the thousands of miles of veins, arteries and capillaries, with devastating effect? It is obviously vital that normal blood in undamaged vessels should not coagulate, and this may be the reason for the complex series of changes that must take place before clotting occurs. The tendency of blood to clot is balanced by the presence of a number of limiting reactions which tend to prevent clotting inside the blood vessels, and to break down the clots that do form. These reactions include the liberation from clotting blood of substances that inhibit further clotting, and the removal of some activated clotting factors from the circulation by the liver. Since the body contains active anti-coagulants (substances which prevent the blood from forming clots while in undamaged vessels), you can imagine how complicated the processes are that turn everything upside down when a wound occurs, allowing the blood to coagulate. It would be no exaggeration to state that at least 12 separate chemical reactions must take place, each by itself enormously complicated, to allow blood to coagulate. It is a step-by-step process, with one reaction activating another factor, which in turn activates another factor, vital links in a chain reaction to turn liquid blood into a solid wall. The absence of any one of those factors or reactions is a serious matter.

A fascinating piece of information is the fact that unborn babies receive their blood directly from their mother, through the placenta. (One of the miracles of birth is the ability of the baby to switch from a dependent blood supply to an independent blood supply within seconds.) In order for the blood to flow easily through the placenta, it perforce lacks many of the coagulating factors that blood normally possesses. Therefore, when the baby is born, it is lacking in those factors, and its clotting capabilities are severely limited. By the eighth day of its life, it has developed all the clotting factors which it requires, and its clotting capability is at its maximum. And it is on the eighth day that we are commanded to circumcise the little boy — an operation whose success depends on the clotting capability of the blood. In the designed world, nothing is coincidental.

Much has not been said: how bones can grow together after being broken; how skin cells multiply to repair the cut; the function of the scab above the wound; the many vital chemical enzymes which exist within the blood without which many reactions in the chain could not happen. But one does not have to understand everything to comprehend that something fantastic takes place in the sealing of a wound and its eventual healing. The complexity of the design, the wisdom of the Creator is indeed breathtaking, and affords us the opportunity for lifelong gratitude. Thank you, Dutch dikes, for a grand lesson!

Silk Tie

Let me tell you a story of long ago. Once upon a time, shortly after the discovery that round wheels run more smoothly than square ones, *yeshivah bachurim* used to wear ties. Take a look at any *yeshivah* photograph of 20 or more years ago, and you will see that the top button of the shirt was closed, and filling the space at the shirt front was a tie. Those of sufficient vintage to remember those far-off days will recall that the tie was an integral part of the male wardrobe, to be worn every single day. Schoolboys wore it as part of their uniform, and all self-respecting males, including *yeshivah bachurim*, considered themselves to some degree undressed without their ties.

Times changed, and with it, the fashion. *Bachurim* began to travel to *Eretz Yisrael*, and began to absorb the air of informality, plus the intense heat, which makes the wearing of a tie something of an idiosyncrasy in Mediterranean countries. Those *bachurim* returned home tieless, and quickly the new fashion spread. Informal, easygoing, young at heart — the open-necked shirt was everything that the modern age yearned for. No matter that in midwinter the open-necked mode meant that you froze, and even two scarves would not keep out the wintry drafts, for fashion you have to be prepared to suffer! Only Shabbos has remained as a safe vestige of the tie's former glory. One day in the week, *baruch Hashem*, people still want to appear decently dressed and smart (but even then, observe how by Shabbos *Minchah* some ties have already been jettisoned!). Ties are for Shabbos — and what ties! Olden-day ties were famous for their drabness, patterns which made you feel drowsy if you looked at them too long, made from synthetic materials. But today? The patterns are bright, loud and gaudy, requiring sunglasses for a close inspection. And the material — it has to be silk! Anything less is just *altmodish* (old-fashioned) in the extreme. No longer will ties be screwed up in the pocket for easy transportation — together with a garment bag and hatbox, the modern young man will be equipped with his portable silk-tie rack!

It must be that the proliferation of popularity in silk ties is the result of intense interest in how silk is produced. And for good reason, for the story is indeed amazing.

To understand how and why a silkworm produces silk, you first have to know a little about the life cycle of a butterfly. The mother butterfly, or moth, lays its eggs. The tiny creature inside the egg is called a caterpillar, and the caterpillar is the child-stage of the adult insect. What trouble these children can be! They eat and grow prodigiously, get into anything and everything, and leave havoc behind them. To be born, the caterpillar eats its way out through the shell of its egg. Usually the egg has been laid on the caterpillar's favorite food plant so that the little glutton can immediately begin its feeding. Because young caterpillars look so tempting to hungry predators, some are protected by a thick coating of hairs, many of which carry an irritant like that of nettles. One species, the pussmoth, can in its young stage put on a false face by pulling down an extra fold of skin. The result is a furious red 'face,' two big scary 'eyes,' and a false fierce 'mouth'!

The next stage in its life is fantastic. The caterpillar begins the restless weaving back and forth of its head that precedes the spinning of its cocoon. The material for the cocoon is produced by glands in the creature's head; it emerges as a viscous fluid which upon contact with air hardens into silk of varying quality. Generally, the cocoon is made in three layers: a coarse, loose outer casing, a lining of fine silken floss, and a papery wrapping around the caterpillar itself. In the dark and silence of this retreat, it passively undergoes its miraculous transformation. On the great day of its exodus, the newly emerging butterfly cuts, or dissolves, or unplugs an opening in its retreat, and crawls out, weak and damp. The wings, crumpled like leaves in bud, slowly expand, their owner waving them, drying and sunning them in the fresh air, until at last they are ready for their maiden flight. The butterfly is equipped with compound eyes which discern color, and a sense of smell which is remarkable. (The antennae of a butterfly bear many sensory structures that are able to detect air movements, vibrations, and smells. It is complex almost beyond description!) Gone is the greed of childhood. These airy adults live only on nectar, reached even in deep-throated flowers by their long, uncurling tongues. Soon enough, somewhere, in the right place, the mother butterfly lays her eggs, and the great cycle of life begins again.

Enter the silkworm. For many long years, silk has been traded from East to West, and it is still the most precious fabric by weight. The next time you decide to buy a silk tie, thank the *bombyx mori*, or domestic silkworm, the caterpillar responsible for spinning the silk fiber to create a cocoon in which it turns into a moth. Each cocoon consists of a single filament up to one mile (1.6 km) long. It takes 110 cocoons to

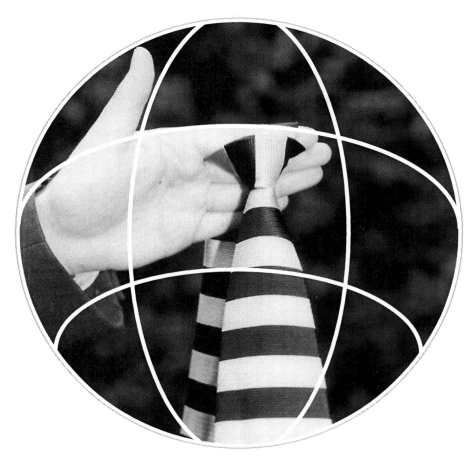

110 silkworms each shook their heads 300,000 times to produce the silk for this Shabbos tie!

make a tie, and 3,000 for a silk *bekeshe*. Silkworms are extremely fastidious in their choice of diet, and although the caterpillars will eat the leaves of a variety of trees, it is well known that mulberry leaves produce the finest silk. Sometimes, we humans try to be too clever. In 1608, King James I of England ordered 10,000 black mulberry trees to be planted across his kingdom to create a domestic silk industry, but the project failed. He had unfortunately chosen the wrong variety — silkworms prefer the white mulberry.

China is the place where most of the silk activity takes place. In fact, for close to 2,000 years, the method of producing silk was a closely guarded secret. Imperial Chinese law decreed that anybody revealing the secret would endure some rather unpleasant Chinese tortures. Now that the secret is out (smuggled out of China by two Persians — who had learned the secret of silk cultivation — along with one ounce of silkworm eggs hidden in their bamboo walking sticks, enough eggs to produce 36,000 silkworms!), it is worth having a closer look at the process, to gain an appreciation of some wonders which otherwise would be taken so much for granted.

Silkworms are raised in the spring, in two months of intensive activity. The eggs, from the previous season, are stored in a cool place and incubated as soon as the mulberry bushes come into leaf. They take about 80 days to hatch; then the worms feed continuously on the mulberry leaves for almost a month. They increase their body weight 10,000 times in this four-week period! (If you would have done the same, you would today weigh some 40 tons, which would be good news for Weight Watchers!) Even breathing does not interfere with their eating, because they breathe through holes in their bodies! Try to picture yourself with your head in a *cholent* bowl, munching incessantly, breathing happily through your knees. You have been designed for your task; the silkworm for his.

The silkworms shed their skin (molt) some four times as they expand in size. After their fourth molting the silkworms set about making their cocoons. They begin to exclude a semiliquid mixture from the two silk glands that run the length of their bodies. The single thread which emerges is made up of the two threads joined together. It is, by the way, just $1/1200$ inch thick. How the silkworm spins its silky cocoon is remarkable. First it anchors itself by making a fine net. Then, tossing its head in a figure-eight motion, it slowly builds up a waterproof cocoon that completely surrounds it. It takes a worm about three days to spin the entire cocoon, during which it will have shaken its head some 300,000 times! Left to its own devices, the worm will turn into a moth in about two weeks, exude an enzyme to weaken the cocoon, and emerge to begin the life cycle once more. In practice, only a few are allowed this luxury, to provide for the following year.

The rest are eliminated! By preventing the cocoon from being damaged by the emerging moth, an unbroken thread can be recovered. The cocoon is then soaked in warm water, and the silk thread is pulled out in a long single strand. The unbroken strands from between five and eight cocoons are twisted together to make silk thread, which is then twisted into skeins. The skeins are dyed, and used either to make fabrics or for embroidery.

It is all so amazing! Here is a tiny creature chewing out of its egg, equipped with a nonstop eating mechanism, which breaks out of its skin four times, capable of producing a thread $\frac{1}{1200}$ of an inch thick, a mile long, whose fibers are not round, but triangular, reflecting the light; capable of producing a complex chemical to dissolve its home after it had performed the miracle of changing from a wriggling caterpillar into a graceful flying moth! Is it any wonder that *yeshivah bachurim* throughout the world give honor to this brilliant display of design by the Creator, by wearing a silk tie on Shabbos *Kodesh*?!

I magine that you are a man from Shakespearean times, who has suddenly been transported from the 1500s to the present time. This does not happen every day, and so, as something of a celebrity, you are given the honor of a grand tour of your vastly updated little town. Having just arrived from an era of 400-year vintage, the contrasts are vast. You remember your little town, the animals in the street (go back to London just a hundred years ago and you would find herdsmen driving their cattle through the streets to market), the motley-shaped huts and houses scattered haphazardly astride the muddy paths that you call streets. Vivid in your memory is the aroma of your town, the constant battle to remain clean, requiring you to tread with care through the mud and garbage, a situation exacerbated by the universally accepted custom of throwing all types of garbage out of the window and into the street below.

You stand amazed as you view your little town now. The streets are straight and of uniform width, the sides of the road are paved and even. Graceful lamps illuminate the town at night, making it safe and pleasant to travel. The cleanliness of the town hits you hard. You learn, to your astonishment, that each house (built of durable brick and of pleasing design, uniform of shape, with garden attached, and all possessing glass windows!) has its own garbage can, which regularly once or twice each week is emptied by paid employees of the town, and safely and hygienically disposed of. Who has ever heard of such comforts! When you are told that more personal waste disappears from each home by means of an internal plumbing system, through a network of underground conduits to a factory where it is chemically treated and rendered harmless, you feel faint with wonder. Open-mouthed, you observe how large oblong boxes with wheels at each corner glide along the smooth roads, each carrying up to 72 passengers, transporting them in comfort and at great speed to their destination. How wonderful is this place! When someone takes you into the large supermarket, where hundreds of articles are tastefully arranged and displayed for sale, many stores in one huge store, you cannot believe your eyes. You visit the library where tens of thousands of books are stored, the sum total of human knowledge, which people may borrow and learn. Terrific!

You think of your archaic settlement, and you look around at this city of the 20th century. What a contrast! So much thought and wisdom must have gone into its planning, a fortune must have been invested by the city planners to create an environment which was both pleasing and efficient. Finding a seat, you sit down and look around. You wonder what all your contemporaries would say if they could see what your eyes are now privileged to behold. They would not believe it! They would be speechless with amazement! Yet strangely enough, all the people who throng the modern city seem particularly unamazed. It's as if they are accustomed to it all, and simply take it all for granted.

Think of a giant chemical factory — acres of pipes, steam and storage tanks. The chemical factory takes substances, breaks them down and builds them up, in highly complex reactions, just like a tiny cell! It staggers the imagination to perceive that in such a tiny entity, there is so much activity, so much planning and purpose, but it is so. Hundreds of chemical changes and reactions occur every second in each living cell. These changes can take place only if the chemical substances are in the form of a watery solution. Water is vital for life of any kind. And here comes another amazing fact. Although water can pass in and out of the cell in an uncontrolled way (because individual water molecules are small enough to pass between the outer cover of the cell — called the membrane — by a process called osmosis), nutrients, minerals and other essential items cannot, because their molecules are too large to pass through the membrane. Incredibly, each cell membrane can regulate the passage of larger molecules, such as proteins, by allowing them entry only at certain sites, which are like entrance and exit doors. By opening and closing these 'doors,' the cell regulates its contents, and keeps a healthy balance of body substances. Do you know of any city which is surrounded by a wall, with an efficient security system at each gate, that developed to its present standard by accident? Is the entry procedure at Ben Gurion Airport, with its computerized list of undesirable applicants, a haphazard arrangement?

The city is organized. It has roads, houses, factory sites and open spaces. A cell is not a random collection of chemicals floating about as if they were in a bowl of soup. Instead, just as the interior space of an office building is organized into useful sections by walls, floors, doors, elevator shafts, windows and stairways, so the cell's interior is highly structured too. Membranes are found not only surrounding the cell as a barrier, but also inside the cell. These membranes curve, bend and fold back on themselves to create tubes, channels, compartments and other structures in which chemicals are organized. And in exactly the same way that the whole body has a framework of bones to give it shape and strength, similarly a cell has a framework. This is made of scaffolding-like microtubules of protein.

The more you investigate your city, the more impressed you become by the coordination and planning of it all. Please come into the cell. What you would be witnessing would be an immense automated factory, a factory larger than a city, and carrying out almost as many unique functions as all the manufacturing activities of man on earth! See the 'Golgi body' (named after the Italian microscope expert, Camillo Golgi, who discovered them), where cell products are packaged in membrane bags before leaving the cell. Have a look at the area within the cell where energy from nutrients is released by complicated chemical reactions to provide the fuel for the body's life processes. Visit the *ribosomes*, where proteins are assembled from amino acids. (Proteins are the body's main construction substance, and are made from building blocks called amino acids.) Did you say that every city has a bus station? Then come to the *endoplasmic reticulum*, the area within the cell where the cell products are assembled and transported. You will remember, won't you, that we are talking about an area many times less than a 100th of the size of the period that you will see . . . now.

There is no doubt whatsoever, that the building which occupies the place of pride in every city is the civic center (alias the town hall, or the city hall). Always an imposing building, usually in the town center, it is the nerve center of the town's administration. It costs millions, takes years to build, but is proclaimed by the city fathers as the ultimate in efficiency. Perhaps. May we show you the tiny cell's civic center? It is to be found in the center of the cell, and is called the nucleus. The nucleus is the cell's control center, and it contains all the genetic information that will ensure that an intestinal cell will behave like such, and not like a brain cell.

Genetic information (genes) are units of inheritance, passed from parents to their offspring. Genes are the plans for each feature of the body, such as bone shape, intestinal structure, and skin color. Genes are sections of the chemical DNA (a story in themselves), packaged into structures called chromosomes, and arranged in pairs inside the nucleus of the cell. Vast quantities of information is stored within the nucleus. In fact the capacity of the DNA to store information vastly exceeds that of any known system. And you thought that the city library was well organized?

Many people are proud of the town where they live. They advertise and encourage tourists to visit and see the grand sights. They may be right, and fully justified. But stand back and give honor to the greatest city of all. You see, a cell has one capacity not equaled in even the most futuristic of cities. There is but one London, no one can duplicate New York, and Yerushalayim is unique. Not so the humble cell. Every one of the vast range of cells can duplicate its entire structure within a matter of a few hours. The cell — complex beyond human comprehension, a veritable city of wonders — is a masterpiece of planning by the Master Intelligence.

A Trillion Invitations

"*azel tov!* You heard who's engaged? What a *simchah!*" If you are a good friend, you will go over to drink a *l'chaim* and give your good wishes. After you have given the *chassan* and the *kallah* your heartiest congratulations, perhaps you would like to give them again — this time to the parents of the happy couple. They'll need it! Forget about the financial obligation (easy to say); their major worry will be whom to invite to the wedding. Some people, well-experienced, non-emotional pragmatic types, say that if you can make a wedding without making any enemies, you can consider it a great achievement! You can well understand. You might be thinking of making a small wedding. Long may you think! You sit down and begin making a list of all your relatives, people who think they are your relatives, friends, people who consider themselves your friends, but won't if they fail to receive an invitation, business associates and social acquaintances, and before you know where you are, the list is enormous! After much agonizing and soul-searching, the list is compiled.

Now comes the difficult part: Making sure that everyone who is on your list receives his invitation. Have you ever seen notices placed in the newspaper stating, "Please accept this as a personal invitation since many invitations have been lost in the mail"? Perhaps it is true, perhaps it is a form of insurance to cover themselves against irate former friends whom they forgot. Did you hear the horror story of the chassan who put all his invitations into the mailbox one evening and found out the next morning that some charming character had inserted burning paper in the same mailbox and burnt every invitation! These things can happen! Even when everything goes according to plan, the physical effort involved in dispatching 300 invitations — each with a different address (where have they moved?), some with a personal note — is enormous. No wonder you heave a hefty sigh of relief when the last envelope drops into the mailbox. Just hope that there is no postal strike! Could you, in your wildest dreams (or nightmares), imagine having to invite 100 million, trillion guests? That is the equivalent of 20,000 invitations to every single person in the world; not only once, but each and every day! Would you consider such a feat possible?

Not only is it possible, but it is actually happening inside you. In your body there is a tiny gland. This gland produces a hormone (a chemical messenger) that is transported to every single cell that you possess. The number of cells that comprise your body is approximately one trillion. This fantastic machine is called the thyroid gland. It is pink in color, resembles a butterfly in shape, and it straddles the windpipe,

Mazel tov Mazel tov! Now comes the difficult part . . .

just beneath the Adam's apple. Some statistics are so re-markable, the human mind finds difficulty in comprehending them. All the more reason to hear them! The thyroid gland weights a grand total of two-thirds of an ounce. The amount of hormone that the thyroid produces is less than $1/100,000$ of an ounce each day. That quantity is so minute that it can hardly be imagined. You might think that a gland with such a diminutive size and tiny production is not very important.

Nothing could be further from the truth. The hormone produced is transported to each cell in the body, and it affects the rate at which the cell burns its fuel to produce energy. The thyroid gland, like all glands in the body's endocrine system, has no ducts or pipes. Instead it releases its hormone directly into the bloodstream. The blood is the mailman, and as it carries the hormone through the body, the hormone comes into contact with each single cell, with vital consequences. It is interesting to know that the 'postal system' operates by means of special enzymes (a type of protein that controls a chemical reaction in the body) which hook molecules of these hormones to blood proteins so that they can hitchhike to the remotest corners of the body. The vital hormone produced by the thyroid gland is called *thyroxine*, and thyroxine controls the metabolism.

Have you ever noticed that there are people who can eat and eat, in enormous quantities, and never put on an ounce of weight? Other people merely have to look at food, and the inches begin to multiply. Why is this? The answer is metabolism. Some people's cells burn the fuel that they consume quickly, and they remain slim, whereas other people burn their fuel more slowly. Each person is different, but everyone's metabolism is controlled by the hormone thyroxine. It is truly incredible how a microscopic difference in the amount of thyroxine produced by the thyroid gland can affect so many physical aspects of our lives. The logic is that since thyroxine stimulates virtually all of your vast multitude of cells (and organs), each with its individual function, many aspects of the body are influenced. If the thyroid produced too little of its vital hormone, the person would feel sluggish, his voice would be husky and slow (the medical profession has a saying that hypothyroidism — an underactive thyroid — is one illness that can be diagnosed over the telephone), and he would have a tendency to obesity. The body would simply run in slow motion. On the other hand, if the thyroid produced a tiny quantity too much of its hormone, the person would develop a wolfish appetite, but would remain thin as he burned up his fuel at a rapid rate. He would feel jittery and nervous, and his pulse would race. The potency of the hormone can be demonstrated by the fact that a tadpole which is deprived of thyroxine will not become a frog.

It is interesting to observe how everything has been created for a specific function ("Do not be disdainful of anything . . . for there is nothing without its place"; Avos 4:3). Take iodine for example. Who needs iodine? Iodine is a chemical present in most drinking water, and in sea foods. Its function? Without it, the thyroid could cease production of thyroxine. Thyroxine is composed of two-thirds iodine. The thyroid chemical factory only requires $\frac{1}{5000}$ gram of iodine (and there are 28 grams in an ounce), yet this microscopic amount spells the difference between vigor and lethargy. Nowadays, iodine is added to salt, so that iodine deficiency is rare.

If the quantity of thyroxine produced by the thyroid gland is so crucial, how precisely does the body 'know' how to regulate it? Just listen to the phenomenal facts! For all effective control, two opposing systems are needed. For example, a car needs an accelerator and brakes. One without the other has no positive function. Similarly, a muscle must have its antagonistic partner, and indeed, most muscles work in pairs, one of them producing movement in one direction, and the other producing the opposite movement. The hormones too have antagonistic effects. This fine balance helps to maintain the correct levels in constantly changing conditions. The balance is maintained partly by the 'feedback' effect of hormones, the system whereby information is fed back to a source, 'telling it' about events in the body, enabling it to adjust its output accordingly. The hypothalamus is a section of the brain that monitors levels of hormones in the blood. When necessary, the hypothalamus sends instructions to the pituitary gland (lying just beneath the brain) to produce a thryoid-stimulating hormone (TSH) to stimulate the thyroid to produce thyroxine. This is kept in check by the fact that when thyroxine reaches the pituitary gland via the circulation, production of TSH is suppressed. The feedback of thyroxine to the pituitary regulates the latter!

If all this was not fantastic enough, hidden within the thyroid gland are four tiny glands called parathyroid glands. Here again we find an amazing example of the design in which complex systems work in perfect harmony and balance within the body. The well-known mineral calcium exists within the blood serum. Within the blood circulation, it plays a vital role in the clotting of blood, muscle contraction, heart function, and the conduction of nerve impulses. There is not much you can do without calcium! On the other hand, too much calcium in the blood can cause kidney stones, with associated groans and moans, not to mention brittle bones. Bones act as a reservoir from which calcium can be drawn to maintain the correct levels in the blood. How does the body know how much calcium should be held in the bones, and how is it transferred from the bones to the blood, and vice versa? What controls the calcium metabolism? Vitamin D (or calciferol) — which is found in fish-liver oil, butter, milk, and cheese — helps the deposition of calcium salts in the bones. Also, natural fats beneath the skin are converted to a form of calciferol by the action of sunlight. If there is a need for more calcium in the blood, and the withdrawal of calcium from the bones, along come our four little glands hidden in the thyroid, and they produce a hormone called *parathormone*. This hormone releases calcium salts from the bones and allows them to enter the blood supply, where they are needed. Once again we meet the feedback system, in which a higher level of calcium in the blood regulates the secretion of parathormone, and the amazing autoregulatory system keeps a perfect balance, and the person in perfect health.

Organizing the century's largest *chasunah* is child's play compared to the everyday work of the thyroid gland. Like everything in the created world, the more you investigate, the more you discover how vastly complicated everything is. Enormously complicated, yet perfectly balanced — all the work of a Master Intelligence of unfathomable wisdom.

Take a Deep Breath

ave you ever heard of the expression 'two left hands'? It means someone who cannot butter his bread without tearing the poor innocent slice to shreds; someone who, when trying to fix a shelf on the wall, uses a hammer to bang in the screws; someone who finds difficulty in sewing a button on a shirt without attaching the sleeves to each other on a permanent basis. These people are often brilliant at poetry, will wax lyrical at a sunset, are giants of intellect, but practical? — never! Fortunately for the progress of mankind, there are clever people around who are also practical. The species with two left hands gaze at these practical marvels with a mixture of awe and bewilderment, for they have no idea at all how people manage to think of such clever ideas. Take, for example, a safety pin. Simple, isn't it? Could you ever have thought of it? Its genius lies in its simplicity, but the impractical among us shake their heads in wonder at the cleverness of the idea that they could never have thought of.

Let me tell you of another invention that leaves members of the two-left-hands society breathless with wonder and admiration. Everyone knows that Orville Wright (a clever American) made the first powered and controlled flight in an airplane in the year 1903. Nearly everyone knows that his plane (called Flyer I) had double wings, and was powered by an engine and two propellers. So far so good. Now until the invention of the jet engine (by an Englishman called Frank Whittle in 1930), all planes had propellers. If you can visualize the types of planes that flew in the First World War, they were usually biplanes, with a single propeller positioned in front of the pilot. During that war, it was obviously considered advantageous for the pilot to be able to fire a machine gun at enemy aircraft. However, how does one fire a machine gun through a propeller without shooting the propeller to bits? You understand the problem? Solve it! It is analogous to asking someone to pass through a revolving door that revolves so fast that it is just a blur — without touching the door. Evidently, someone was able to design the mechanism to make it possible, because by the end of the First World War, both sides in the conflict had planes that were successfully firing machine guns through their propellers. How did they do it? I have absolutely no idea.

If you can sympathize with those who find the propellers' problem difficult to solve, how would you cope with the following? Imagine that you have two balloons in a container, and these balloons have to be inflated and deflated every four or five seconds. You are not allowed to touch the balloons or blow into them; it must all be achieved automatically. If for any reason the mechanism that you must invent fails for

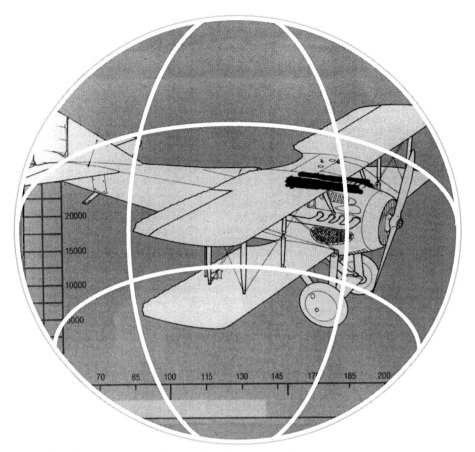

How do you fire a machine gun through your propeller without shooting it to bits?

longer than a minute or two, the consequences would be catastrophic. It could even be life-threatening. How would you do it? If you substitute the word 'lungs' for 'balloons,' you will soon understand the subject under discussion, and its vital importance to us all. The question, simply put, is this. How do you ensure that air, with its life-giving oxygen, is drawn into your two lungs, when those lungs resemble two loose-hanging balloons contained within the chamber called your chest? Two left hands or not, you have to know! How will you do it? How does inhalation work? What clever mechanism allows you to breathe?

You might think that all that is required is to suck air into your mouth or into your nose. It sounds simple enough, until you begin to think a little deeper. How do you suck air? You cannot suck air with your fingers, or with your ears, so how do you manage to achieve it with your mouth? The answer is that the movement of breathing is powered by muscles, but not muscles within the lungs, for the simple reason that the lungs themselves do not contain not one single muscle! Rather, it is the muscles within the chest that cause the chest to expand, forcing air into the lungs. When the same muscles cause the chest to contract, air is forced out of the lungs. Looked at more closely, it works in a most marvelous manner, which certainly is deserving of our attention.

At the base of the chest cavity (called the *thoracic cavity*) lies a dome-shaped sheet of muscle by the name of the diaphragm. You wish to breathe? Do the following: Using the power of your muscles, move the diaphragm downwards, so that instead of being dome-shaped, it becomes flattened. This will increase the size of the chest cavity in a top-to-bottom direction. Again using a complicated arrangement of muscles, swing your ribs outwards and upwards. This will increase your chest cavity in a side-to-side direction. At the same time, move your breastbone forward slightly so that the chest cavity is increased in a front-to-back direction as well. (You will realize that in order to achieve these actions, your rib cage, which you might have thought was as rigid as a block of concrete, is in fact flexible and pliable. It's all part of the design!)

All these movements result in an increase in the volume of the thorax (chest cavity). This now creates a negative pressure — a suction force — inside the thorax. The result is that the walls of the lungs are pulled outwards and air is drawn into them. You may breathe a sigh of relief, for you have now breathed. Breathing out is achieved by the reverse process. The ribs swing downwards and inwards, the breastbone moves back slightly, and the diaphragm bows upwards. The volume of the thorax decreases, and this creates an increased pressure inside it. The result is that air is forced out of the lungs. What is particularly remarkable is that the diaphragm, whose downward movement creates the partial vacuum that draws air into the lungs, is actually perforated in three places. This is to allow the food pipe and the two main highways that lead to and from the heart access to the lower section of the body. The seal around these three pipes must be absolutely perfect, otherwise the downward movement of the diaphragm would achieve precisely nothing. Impressed?

Nothing in a designed world happens by accident. If our lungs were made of non-elasticated material, they would be as useless as two tin cans hanging in our chest. Instead, they are constructed from spongy elasticated tissue, which has remarkable qualities of expansion. Although when sitting quietly and relaxing (as you are doing now!) you breathe in only about half a liter of air with each breath, your lungs have the capacity to hold six liters of air. It is often thought that the lungs empty completely each time you breathe out, but this is not so. When you are sitting quietly (as you are still doing) you breathe in approximately half a liter of air, and breathe out the same quantity. However, about three liters of air remain in your lungs after you have exhaled. The air which is taken in and pushed out with each breath is called 'tidal air,' while the amount staying in the lungs after each breath is called 'residual air.' The two mix together, so that fresh oxygen penetrates deep into your lungs every time you breathe!

Did you know that during World War II, submarine crews were encouraged to sleep as much as possible? This is because during sleep the body is relatively still and needs less oxygen, and in the confined space of a submarine, oxygen is a precious commodity. When you sleep, breathing becomes slower and more regular. When you exercise, you breathe more quickly, because your muscles are working harder, and require extra oxygen. In addition, the carbon dioxide that they produce must be removed quickly, otherwise it could build up and poison the tissues. Now comes the important question. How do you know at what rate to breathe? How do you know if carbon dioxide is building up? Who will tell you? We need an answer, and quickly! Calm down. You do not need to think about it, for it happens automatically. Breathing is controlled by the respiratory center in the brain. This vital control center continually checks the levels of oxygen and carbon dioxide in the blood. It is an amazingly sensitive chemical detector. As soon as it detects the increased acidic level of the blood caused by the build-up of carbon dioxide during exercise, it orders the respiratory system to work at a faster rate. If the level rises even higher, as it does when you perform heavy exercise, it will order you to breathe *deeply* as well as rapidly. It is all part of the remarkable automatic system.

We can change our breathing if we so wish (for example, when whistling or blowing up a balloon), and we can also hold our breath for a short time. However, the body has been designed with a 'fail-safe' mechanism, and will never let breathing stop for too long. Even if a child in a temper is foolish enough to hold his breath until he turns a faint blue, or even faints, there is no need to be too alarmed. Long before he could get into any real trouble, automatic respiration would take over. He would start breathing whether he liked it or not.

The system that enables us to breathe is clever, very clever. Whether or not we are the practical sort, or completely impractical, for every single breath that we take until we reach 120, it is good for us to know just something of the wisdom and sophistication of the design so that we can offer our gratitude to the One Who designed it all.

"עַל כָּל נְשִׁימָה וּנְשִׁימָה שֶׁאָדָם נוֹשֵׁם צָרִיךְ לְקַלֵּס לְהקב"ה"

One must praise Hashem for each breath.

The Great Air Show

nce upon a time, when life was simple, an outing meant a visit to the park. Feeding the ducks plus a ride on the merry-go-round was fun. Try tempting an over-*bar mitzvah* youth with the simple life in today's sophisticated age. Are you serious? It has to be at the very least interesting, certainly exciting, and if possible adventurous. So you will find a proliferation of theme parks, each competing with each other to provide the ultimate in 'knuckle gripping, terrifying, living nightmare, tortuous' fun. How about an air show? Now you're talking. That is something that will grip everyone's imagination. Bombers flying low overhead, filling the sky and shaking the very earth with their brooding, threatening presence; helicopters clattering tantalizingly close; vertical take-off jets tearing the earth apart with their volcanic-roar eruption as, swathed in smoke and flame, they roar into the air — that's what you call an outing. The whole experience is mesmerizing. You can be certain that no one will complain that it was dull.

There is no doubt that flight fascinates. The larger the plane, the greater the fascination. If you ever have the occasion to travel on a Boeing jumbo jet, pause at the bottom of the stairs and view the monstrous machine before you. It is just so enormous, all of 350 tons (and still they make such a fuss about your extra 10 pounds!), as high as a five-story building, as long as a football field, with engines that are cavernous, that you wonder how the whole towering colossus can ever take to the air! As you sit strapped to your seat, surrounded by 499 fellow passengers, hurtling along the runway at 180 mph, you cannot help but be impressed by the power of the engines, the skill of the pilot and the consummate wisdom of the designers that make the whole venture possible.

Go for a stroll in the park. Walk quietly behind a group of nodding pigeons, and suddenly make your presence known. Watch how they flap their wings furiously, 'clapping' them as they soar vertically to the safety of the nearest rooftop. If you ever stop at the side of an expressway, where blackbirds love to gather (the vibrations of the passing traffic loosen the earth bordering the road and tempt worms to the surface where the waiting blackbirds provide a welcoming committee), observe how, with a few sweeps of their great black wings, they become airbone. Almost immediately they retract their legs underneath to assume a more streamlined shape, just like a plane which retracts its wheels — or is it the other way around! Gaze at the aerobatic display of sea gulls as they soar and glide effortlessly through the sky, imperceptibly moving a muscle to change direction before landing, with a shake of their wings, on the rim of a chimney pipe. They never miss, nor do they think highly of their achieve-

The effortless mastery of a swan in flight

ment. But we, the landlocked viewers, because we see it every day, tend not to see it at all. If we could open our minds to the amazing sights that are around us always, realize the complexity and sophistication of the flight systems involved, and become aware of the design, then we might be doing ourselves the greatest favor.

How does it all work? Here is something to comfort you. The mechanics of bird flight are extremely complicated — more so than for an airplane with fixed wings — and some aspects are still not fully understood. Some things, however, we can understand. When gliding, a bird's wing behaves like an airplane's wing, and lift is generated by its forward movement through the air. The bird's wing is shaped to generate lift. It works like this. The upper surface of the wing is convex (curved outwards), causing the airstream to travel further and faster over the wing than beneath the wing. This creates lower pressure above the wing, and higher pressure beneath it, causing the air to push up against the wing, creating lift. (Try it yourself. Take a sheet of paper, and hold the nearest edge with two hands close to your mouth. Gently blow. You will see that the loose end of the paper begins to rise. By blowing the air above the paper, you have created an area of low pressure — a partial vacuum — and the higher pressure beneath the paper forces the paper to lift.) In effect, the bird's wings are similar to an airplane's wings, convex above, concave below, with the leading edge blunt and rounded, and the trailing edge narrowing to a point. When gliding, the bird's wing is behaving like an airplane's wing, and lift is generated by its forward movement through the air, but in flapping flight, the wing is acting as both a lifting surface and a propeller.

There are some amazing facts about the way that a bird flies. A bird that flies slowly faces the same problem as a slow-moving plane. That is, the airflow over the same wing can become turbulent, and lift disappears. When that happens, the wing is said to 'stall.' The bird has been provided with a special refinement called an *alula*, which is a bunch of three or four feathers attached to the bird's 'thumb.' When there is a danger of stalling, the alula is raised, and a stream of rapidly moving air is directed over the wing surface to eliminate turbulence. Herons and storks have a very large alula to give maximum lift on landing, when they almost hover and gently touch down on their long, spindly legs. Hummingbirds have wings that beat like propellers at the rate of 75 beats per second — too fast for the eye to perceive except as a blur. (Try and shake your finger as fast as possible — you'll be lucky to achieve four shakes in a second.) They can hover perfectly, keeping their bills quite still as they suck nectar from flowers. As it hovers, the hummingbird's wings twist into the shape of a propeller, and the wingtips move in a figure-eight to give perfect control. You might have noticed, as dusk falls, enormous flocks of starlings (sometimes numbering millions) gathering together to roost. When they take to the air, they twist, turn and change direction almost as one. No one knows how such perfect harmony is achieved among so many birds.

How long could you run without stopping? A man is considered an Olympic champion if he can gallop along for two or three hours, covering a distance of 25 miles. What do you say about the young swift, which dives out of its nest in Britain for the first time, and flies off to Africa? It returns to a nest site two or three years later, having covered about 44,750 miles, probably without ever stopping. How about the sooty tern, which takes off over the vast oceans, and continues to fly for three or four years without ever settling on water or land! How do these birds manage to generate such a high and continuous output of power? Even less dramatic examples of flying prowess require power as much as a simple car needs an engine. What are the special features that enable the bird to take to the heavens?

In the majority of animals, the skeleton is the heaviest part of the body, but many of the bones of birds are honeycombed with air space. Additional strength is imparted by a crisscross of internal bracing struts, similar to the frame of an airplane (or, more accurately, the airplane has internal bracing struts modeled on the bird). Jaws and teeth, which are the heaviest structures in other animals' bodies, are absent. In their place sits the horny bill. The power of flight is generated in the breast muscles, which, in pigeons, make up one third of the body weight. To supply the flight muscles with the necessary fuel, and the oxygen for burning it, birds are equipped with highly efficient circulation and breathing systems. The heart is much larger than in comparably sized mammals — and it beats at a fantastic rate — 600 beats a minute in the robin, and 1,000 beats a minute in the tiny hummingbird.

The birds' breathing system is unique. As well as the usual pair of lungs found in all other warm-blooded animals, they have special air sacs spread throughout their bodies; within muscles, abdominal organs, and even in the hollow of their bones. The sacs are connected to the lungs and wind-pipe by a complicated arrangement of tubes and shunts. This unique system creates a one-way flow through the lungs by the air shuttling between the air sacs, as distinct from the tidal to-and-fro system in mammals. It is an outstanding ef-ficient system, not only for normal flight, which is strenuous enough, but particularly for high-altitude flying where the air is rarefied. Many birds regularly fly at over 5,000 feet on their migratory journeys (birds have been seen flying happily over Mt. Everest at 27,000 feet), and the cross-current flow explains how they survive flight at such altitudes.

Everything about the bird declares the wisdom of its Designer. Birds never fall off branches when they go to sleep. They naturally (!) grip any branch they land on, as their feet automatically lock into position with the toes clamped around the branch. Who taught them the trick? The toucan has a beak which is as long as its body, but very light and extremely strong. The beak has serrated edges, like teeth, to enable it to slice through its food! Who told the toucan that a serrated blade is more efficient than a smooth one? Pelicans have beaks with giant pouches of soft, elastic skin, which they use to scoop up fish from water. Fully stretched under-water, it can hold about 13 liters (3 gallons) of water. It then shrinks to squeeze out the water before the fish is swallowed. Who advised it to grow its beak to bucket-size, and how do you shrink a bucket?

Birds, like all animals, display skills and wonders which are completely beyond their own knowledge. (And even if they did know about them, you try and grow some wings, or grow a beak, or completely alter your breathing system!) Where there is intelligence, there is a Designer. Give yourself a real treat — go to the park, feed the ducks, and watch the greatest air show on earth.

The Parachute Regiment

T he Major General looked grim, and with good reason. For months now the battle with the enemy had been in a position of stalemate. Each side was entrenched in their network of well-defended positions, facing each other over a wasteland pockmarked with craters. The whole campaign was an exercise in frustrating futility. Each time one side tried to advance, they were repulsed with horrendous loss of life. Morale among the troops was low, with both sides locked in a conflict that threatened to continue forever. It was for this reason that the Major General had called a meeting of his top officers and military advisers. Something had to be done to break the impasse.

"Gentlemen," began the revered leader, observing the men sitting around the long oval table with the practiced eye of a man well used to surveying the opposition, "I have called this meeting for one reason only. We must achieve victory, and it must be achieved quickly. We cannot afford more casualties, yet the military situation appears deadlocked. I have invited you all here to give your suggestions. You may speak your minds without fear of ridicule — but I beg you to apply your intelligence to the saving of life and the procuring of victory." Gravely he sat down, and a heavy silence pervaded the room. What could anyone suggest that had not already been tried? Suddenly, a young man stood up, and, hesitantly at first, but with increased passion, began to speak.

"What I would like to suggest is revolutionary. The problem seems to be one of breaking through the enemy lines. We have tried every method that exists on the ground. But what about the air? Let us make birds of metal that can fly, large enough for soldiers to sit inside. The bird would soar over enemy territory, and our soldiers, heavily armed, would then jump out of the bird, holding large umbrellas to enable them to glide safely to earth. They could then attack from behind enemy lines in conjunction with our conventional advance, and victory would be assured." He sat down, flushed with his own rhetoric. There was a moment of unbelieving silence, quickly broken by a single guffaw, which grew into a chorus of laughter and ridicule which rolled and echoed from wall to wall. The Major General was not amused. He rose ponderously to his feet, and with a look of withering disdain in the direction of the speaker, asked if there were any serious suggestions!

Poor young man. He lived a hundred years too soon. If the Major General would have been around in the latter half of the 20th century, he could have observed squadrons of metal birds flying at close to the speed of sound, with elite troops tumbling headfirst from open doorways, descending to the ground at the rate of 20 feet a second, by means of nylon parachutes. The very first parachute jump from an airplane

The delicate parachutes poised for takeoff

was made in 1912. Soon after World War I, an American, Leslie Irvin, designed an improved parachute which he tried out himself. After some 50,000 official tests, it was adopted by the American and British air forces. Since that time, parachute regiments have become an integral part of every modern army, while parachuting itself, in the guise of skydiving, has become an opportunity for thousands to experience the exhilaration of floating through space.

What a shame that the Major General walked around with closed eyes. Had he but the eyes to see, he could have observed parachutists too numerous to count. Stroll along any street, and look around. There is no doubt that the most prolific flower is the dandelion. For some reason, it does not enjoy great popularity; indeed it is even considered a weed. Like so many things in life, its great abundance discourages people from noticing it. But it is just those things that everyone takes so much for granted that deserve the greatest scrutiny. Let us take a close look at one of the greatest wonders of all time!

The dandelion's flower is characteristically bright yellow. It opens in the morning, waiting to be pollinated by a passing insect (the color only make sense if the insects enjoy color vision, which they do), and closes in the afternoon or when it rains. Ever thought how you open a flower or close it? Wow! After opening and closing for a number of days, during which time it may be pollinated, the flower finally closes, and seed formation begins. Gradually, the yellow petals wither away, and the seed heads begin to form. These seeds are its children, and they are protected by an all-enclosing green bract. Within the green bracts, wonders are happening. Each and every one of the hundred of seeds is attached by the slenderest of stalks to a silky parachute — its flight ticket to freedom. At first, the parachutes are squashed together, but as the bracts around the edge of the seed head fold back, the parachutes expand and separate. (Imagine hundreds of parachutes for your favorite regiment tangled together in a sticky mess, miraculously unraveling themselves in time for the big drop! Impressed?)

The dandelion now resembles a ball of fluff. Attached to a central launching pad are hundreds of tiny fruits, containing the seeds of future generations, all awaiting takeoff. The degree of adhesion that attaches the seeds to the pad is crucial. If it were too strong, it could never detach. If it were too weak, the seed would just fall to the ground. Needless to say, it is perfect! Now the seeds are ready to go. If the air is still, the fruits may spend several days attached to the seed head. This is a dangerous time for them, because seed-eating birds are likely to peck them off for supper. A slight breeze is all that is needed to lift the parachutes into the air. They may fall close by, but if there is enough updraft they can be carried for long distances. When a fruit lands, it no longer needs the parachute that has carried it on its journey, and this breaks off. (We have to understand what a simple statement like this implies. When a human parachutist falls to the ground, his harness is fitted with a quick release mechanism so that the airman can detach himself from the parachute as soon as he reaches the ground, otherwise he may be dragged along and badly bruised. Who taught the humble dandelion the art of quick release!?) Over the winter, the seed sinks into the soil, waiting for the spring when it begins to germinate.

If you think that a parachute is a complex mechanism, then how about plants that disperse their seeds with natural catapults? These work by suddenly releasing tension that builds up as the seedcase grows. The seedcase splits open, flinging the seeds in all directions. These catapults are triggered in a number of ways. Some, particularly the pods of pea-family plants such as vetches, burst open when the sun dries them. Others, such as the Himalayan balsam, are triggered by movement, either by the wind blowing past, or by an animal brushing against the plant. It must always be remembered that plants rely on seed dispersal to survive to the next generation. Whatever mechanism they use, be it parachute or catapult, has to work perfectly, otherwise it is of no value. A catapult without elasticity is a sad flop, and half a parachute is a recipe for disaster. Exemplifying as they do perfection in design, they must always have functioned as they do now, otherwise they would not be here to prove the point!

The aforementioned perfection in design is dazzling. The milkweed plant also uses parachutes to spread its seeds. The fluffy white fibers are so efficient that they can float on the wind for many kilometers. The fibers are so light that they have even been used to fill life jackets, which keep people afloat in water. Would you like to hear an ingenious method of spreading your seeds? Your seed might be too heavy to be carried away by parachute; if so, an animal carrier might be more appropriate. Therefore, ensure that your seed develops inside a tasty berry, which should be brightly colored and attractively tasting to tempt the customer. However, beware!

If your precious seed is going to be consumed by an animal or bird (or even humans who enjoy eating tomatoes and water melons), you have to know precisely how strong the intestinal juices are of that creature, and coat your seed with a cover sufficiently strong to withstand the acidic environment! The durian fruit attracts many mammals with its strange smell. It may grow as large as a football and has custard-like flesh around the seed. When animals (the durian is a favorite food of the orangutan) eat the fruits, the seeds pass through their bodies unharmed and fall to the ground where they germinate, a good distance from the parent fruit. Have you ever met any ocean travelers? Did you know that coconuts float away from their parent trees on the ocean currents? They may drift for several months and travel for up to 2,000 kilometers before reaching dry land. Special fibers around the seeds help the coconut to float. I wonder which came first, the urge to travel by sea, or the special fibers!

Major General! You are surrounded by parachutes, catapults, ocean-going vessels, and agents that can enter the enemy's very innards and exit unscathed. Every single dandelion is a parachute regiment, demonstrating a greater degree of precision and design than anything a human could achieve. They are all around — a slight breeze is all that is needed to lift the parachutes into the air — and a slight amount of thought is all that is needed to transform those parachutes into tangible *emunah.*

The Remarkable Rubber Tree

We don't want to worry you, but we have a little problem. You see, we have this rather large 350-ton jumbo jet that has requested permission to land. There are no other aircraft in the area, so we can easily give permission. We even have an extended runway, certainly sufficiently long to cater to the runaway giant. The airplane has wheels, and plenty of them, so that doesn't present any difficulties. The problem is that the captain of the jumbo has not yet decided what material to place around the metal rim of those numerous and ponderous wheels. You have to visualize the situation to appreciate the scope of the problem. A jumbo jet is enormous in size, and as it descends from the sky to meet *terra firma*, it is traveling at some 200 miles an hour. As contact is made between the wheel rim and concrete, the friction created is intense! So quickly, suggest what he can use! Should he wrap the rims with sacking, a material which is usually very hard wearing? It will rip to shreds in a second. Should he clothe the wheels in leather? The jolt caused by the impact will snap off the wheels as easily as a fragile twig. Perhaps he should simply leave the wheels in their pristine steel? Could you imagine the steel wheel carving a trench in the concrete, with sparks pouring forth, each spark posing the gravest risk? We have to find the solution, and quickly!

While I think, my mind tires. Tires? You mean tires? That's it! Rubber tires — the perfect solution. An inflated ring of rubber that covers the rim of the wheel will absorb the impact, is strong and durable, waterproof and flexible. The problem has been solved — what a relief. Imagine now that you had to describe this substance called rubber to a newcomer to Earth. What would you like to say? "Well, it's sort of black and elasticated, you know, like . . . rubber!" But where does it grow, how is it made, who discovered it, why do we need it, and could we ever manage without it? The answer to the last question is a definite no, as anyone who has ever traveled in a car, plane or bicycle will attest. Imagine the level of discomfort as you ride — or rather bounce and jolt — along the highway at 70 mph in a car with wheels bound by metal! As to the answer to the first questions, prepared to be amazed.

Why is rubber so useful? There are many reasons. It holds air (as in your balloon), it keeps out moisture (as in your rubber boots), it does not readily conduct electricity (which explains its wide use in insulation), and is a poor conductor of heat (making it an excellent choice of materials with which to coat the handles of frying pans). But its chief importance to us is that it is elastic. In fact, rubber can be made so elastic that it will stretch to more than nine times

Imagine racing along at 70 mph on wooden wheels!

its normal length. When you stretch a rubber band and let it go, its elasticity makes it quickly spring back to its original shape. A rubber ball, that mainstay of children's games, bounces because of this same springiness. Your rubber heels are wonderful shock absorbers because of their elasticity. Fantastic stuff, rubber, but where does it come from?

When the early European explorers came to Central and South America, they saw the Indians playing with bouncing balls made of rubber. According to an early Spanish historian, Columbus found the Indians using balls 'made from the gum of a tree.' The explorers learned that the Indians made 'waterproof' shoes from the *latex*, the milky white juice of the rubber tree. They spread the latex on their feet, and let it dry. Those same Indians also made waterproof bottles by smoothing latex on a bottle-shaped clay mold. They dried the latex over a fire, and then washed out the clay. It was not until the 18th century that two French scientists spent several years on botanical research in South America. In 1730, one of them, Monsieur Francois Fresneau, made a full report about rubber, and was the first scientist to describe the rubber tree. Another major breakthrough took place in 1823. It was in that year that a Scottish manufacturer, Charles Macintosh, had a brilliant idea for raincoats. He rubberized two pieces of cloth with dissolved rubber, and pressed them together, making a sort of cloth sandwich with a rubber filling. Although these coats became popular, they were not perfect, as the rain leaked in at the seams, and in hot weather, the rubber leaked out.

While Mr. Macintosh was trying to perfect his raincoats, an American by the name of Charles Goodyear was attempting to produce rubber that would not be affected by changes of temperature. Then, one day in 1839, he accidentally placed a mixture of rubber, white lead and sulphur on a hot stove. (Some accident!) When he removed it, he found that the rubber could still be stretched, but had not become gummy. Thus he discovered the process known as vulcanization, whereby heating sulphur with rubber, the compound remains tough and firm in both heat and cold. Vulcanized rubber was elastic, airtight and watertight. It could be used to make tight seals between the moving parts of machinery. The rubber industry had begun.

So much for the work of man. But what of the actual substance, and the trees from which it stems? Latex is found in a wide variety of trees and other plants. (You can see latex oozing from the broken stem of a dandelion.) One thing is clear: We cannot manage without rubber. But what latex actually is, is still a mystery to men of knowledge. Scientists know that latex is not a sap, but they are not sure of its use to the plant. There are those who think that latex acts as a kind of protective substance when a plant has been wounded.

If so, why do some trees have latex in superabundance (such as the rubber tree) and so many have none? As we shall see, the answer to the question is that the Creator of the Universe knew that mankind would need rubber, so He created latex!

The milky liquid called latex consists of about 30 to 35 percent pure rubber. Water accounts for another 60-65 percent, with the remainder formed by resins, proteins and sugar. The latex holds tiny globules (particles) of rubber in the same way that milk holds butterfat. The rubber tree (known officially as the *hevea tree*) grows best in hot, moist climates. The latex which contains the rubber flows through a series of tubes in the layer of the tree directly under the bark. When this layer is pierced, the latex oozes out.

Plantation workers (known as 'tappers') begin work at day-break, because the latex flows most freely in the cool morning air. The tapper removes a thin shaving of bark with a tool shaped so that the bottom of the groove forms a channel. The groove slants diagonally downward about halfway around the trunk. At the bottom of the cut, the tapper attaches a U-shaped metal spout, and below that, a small cup. The latex oozes from the inner bark, and flows down the channel into a collecting cup. Don't feel sorry for the cut bark — as the latex dries, it seals the cut! Each tapper works on about 350 trees on one round of tapping. This task takes him about three hours. After tapping the last tree, the tapper make a second round to collect the latex, removing the dried latex and making a fresh cut. Rubber trees yield their full capacity of latex for about 25-30 years, and 'champion' rubber trees can produce more than 10 kilograms of rubber a year. What is amazing is that after about three or four years, the grooves in the tree reach the ground. The tapper then goes to the other side of the tree, and begins cutting the bark there. By the time the second set of grooves reaches the ground, the bark has grown back on the first grooves, and it is ready to be tapped again!

Rubber is a wonder product. We depend on it so much that it would be almost impossible to manage without it. This is not the case with other materials. If we lack one material, we can substitute with another. A house can be built from brick, stone or wood. Clothes can be made from cotton, wool or silk. But what about the tires on that jumbo jet, rapidly approaching the runway, or car, truck and bus? You cannot imagine making them of anything but rubber. Only rubber is elastic, airtight, water resistant, shock absorbing, and resilient. Manufacturers make between 40,000 and 50,000 rubber products. A typical car has about 600 rubber parts. The world's largest tire contains over 3,200 kilograms of natural rubber. Think of waterproof aprons, boots, raincoats, hot-water bottles, ice bags, elastic bands, bathing caps, goggles, rubber life-rafts, golf balls, tennis balls, bottle stoppers, rubber gloves and shoe soles. How could we manage without it? Our whole transport system is dependent on rubber. More than half the rubber used in the world goes into tires and tubes, which in turn are fitted onto cars, airplanes, bicycles, trucks, tractors, and construction machinery. Modern society would quite literally grind to a halt without this amazing fruit of the rubber tree.

Everything that has been created has been created for a purpose. Who could have known that the humble juice of the hevea tree would one day keep the wheels of society running smoothly? The Creator of the Universe knew that one day mankind would require the services and qualities of rubber — for 50,000 different products — and so the rubber tree, with its everflowing latex, was created to satisfy that need. Thank you, Hashem, for the rubber tree — whenever we take a ride in a car, or land in a jumbo jet — we will acknowledge the wonders of Your World of Wisdom.

The Ferrari F50 and You

o you want to hear a sad story? It's not so sad really, but it did happen. Once upon a time, there was a young man who had spent many years in *yeshivah*. Eventually the time came for him to leave, and he obtained a position as a Rabbi in a small suburban community. As the congregants were widely scattered, he decided that a car would be an essential asset. Never having owned a car, and being just a little naive, he withdrew his total wealth — which amounted to a few hundred dollars — from the bank, went to a second-hand car dealer, and asked him if he could supply him with a vehicle for the sum in his possession. The dealer took one look at the gullible guy, and decided that he had just the car for him. Taking him around to the back of the garage, he showed the eager customer an old jalopy, with almost as many miles on the clock as there are Chinamen in China. Assuring him that it was a 'terrific little runabout,' the car and the money soon changed hands. Everything went reasonably well until one bright day, when as the rabbi was turning a sharp corner, he heard a loud crack and felt a jolting lurch. The back axle had snapped. The 'terrific little runabout' had run its last. The moral of the story is that if you have very limited funds available, buy a bike!

If, on the other hand, money is no object, you may be interested to hear about one of the most expensive cars in the world. The fact is, you cannot buy Ferrari's latest supercar, the F50, even if you have the required $500,000. The company calculated that there were 350 potential customers in the world, so they built one less than demand, and all 349 cars are sold. Would you like to know some details? It is a two-seater, big, red and noisy, but has a top speed of 202 mph. If you are in a hurry, it can move from a standstill to 62 mph in 3.8 second. Its enormous engine has five valves per cylinder, and has the power equal to that of 520 horses. It is a blend between a Formula One racing car and a fighter plane, and it is definitely not the car for a new rabbi.

You can imagine that any one of the 349 owners of the F50 would feel that their money has been well spent. They would point to the stylish design, the superb performance, and the feeling of exclusiveness with which their car has endowed them. Pity that they had to spend half a million dollars (the equivalent of the annual budget of a small *yeshivah*) to acquire that feeling. They could have saved their wealth (or donated it to the fair-sized *yeshivah*), looked in the mirror, and for no money at all gazed at a machine which makes their precious F50 look like the rabbi's old jalopy.

Look at some of the features. What would happen if, on your next visit to the garage, you filled the fuel tank with diesel fuel instead of gasoline? Billowing smoke, throaty gurgles, and

The sleek and powerful Ferrari . . . almost as good as — you!

eventually a stubborn refusal to budge would indicate the car's displeasure at the change of diet. Strange really, because both gasoline and diesel are oil derivatives, yet the slightest variation can wreak havoc. Now look at yourself. The variety of diet that the human digestive system can assimilate is simply astonishing. You hear stories of Jews who during the war survived on a diet of tulip bulbs. There was once a Frenchman who lived happily on a diet of metal. (Perhaps he is now rusting in peace!) Supermarket carts are not everyone's idea of a Rosh Chodesh treat, but he managed. Organic food, health food, fruit, fish, meat, milk, sugar, alcohol, minerals fats and oils . . . the stomach welcomes them all, and keeps the machine running smoothly. Think about what you consume over a Shabbos, imagine putting all that into your car's gas tank, and ask yourself which machine has the superior design.

With expensive cars come expensive worries. What happens if someone comes a little too close, and scratches the gleaming paintwork, or knocks a dent into the delicate bodywork? For a car of that price, you should expect it to repair itself! You can expect to your heart's content. Prepare for a disappointment, for nothing repairs itself — except your very own body. The fact that bones can so readily repair themselves, if fractured, is nothing short of miraculous. When a limb is fractured, a whole host of rescue services answer the emergency. Torn blood capillaries form a clot. Macrophages (cells which are mobile rubbish disposal units) invade the clot and devour the debris. In answer to a secret signal, bone cells multiply and move into the blood clot where they lay down new bone tissue. In the mending process, a ring of new bone tissue is formed around the fracture, so the mended bone is slightly thicker in the region of the fracture — rather like the joint which a plumber makes when connecting two lengths of pipe. The new bone i
s remodeled; any unwanted bits are broken down and reabsorbed. Ossification, calcification, resorption and deposition are just some of the stages in the miracle that can self-repair a break so effectively that the final mend is almost undetectable in an X-ray. Then think about your skin that repairs itself so effectively ... How much would you pay for a car that repairs itself? You have it all, and more, free of charge.

No car is immune. The salesman may tell you that for the first two years it is free, but you still have to bring it in for service. You give over your machine to their — you hope — competent hands and hope that they will do what they claim to do. Change the oil, check the plugs, replace the brake-pads and refill the fluids — it is all part of keeping your car in good condition. Not with your body! What would happen if you lived sensibly, and never once went to the doctor? You would be just fine. All the body fluids, from the hydrochloric acid in your digestive system, the blood that courses through the thousands of miles of capillaries, the liquid chemical cleaner that cleans your eyes, the germ-killing saliva in your mouth, the vitreous humor that fills your eyes and gives them shape, the lubricating synovial fluid that enables you to move your joints — all of them are constantly being used and replaced. We eat whatever we like, and cheerfully expect the fantastic chemical factory of our body to produce all the chemicals, the enzymes and the formulae to keep us going. And it does! Not only are the fluids replaced, but every single part of our bodies is constantly being renewed. You are not the same person you were a month ago! Your skin, your bones, your hair — every single cell is replenished, refreshed and replaced on a regular basis. There is no car to match us. The human body has no dipstick. It is all breathtakingly automatic.

If you leave your car unattended in the summer, two things are likely to happen on your return. One is that you might find a parking ticket on your window (that can happen in the winter, too!) and the second is that as you open the door, a wall of hot air rises to greet you. Cars are notorious heat-traps, and leaving animals (*kal v'chomer*, small children) in cars with the windows closed can be extremely hazardous. The more expensive cars have an air-conditioning system which, if correctly set, maintains a constant cool temperature in even the severest heat. With cars it is an expensive extra — with humans it is standard! Whether you live in the burning deserts of Libya or the frozen wastes of Greenland, your body temperature will always remain a constant 98.6 degrees Fahrenheit. You don't have to think about it, set it, recharge the batteries, clean the fan, or add a drop of oil — summer or winter, tropics or North Pole, your personal body thermostat should give you 120 trouble-free years of satisfaction.

All cars, from the most humble to the vaunted Rolls Royce, run on tires. The rubber tires are not solid, but inflated with air. The last thing you want to hear as you approach your car is a steady hissing sound from the direction of one of the wheels. Puncture! Similarly, an ominous dripping from beneath the fuel tank, or a tell-tale pool of water forming beneath the radiator, are sights that you do not want to see. It seems that neither the tire nor the fuel tank, or even the radiator, have a self-sealing feature that would render them immune to the dreaded drip — not even the celebrated F50 costing a cool half-a-million. Strange, really, because your body copes very well. When the doctor gives an injection, he is actually puncturing the skin, and, more to the point, making a hole in the vein. That vein is nothing less than a fuel pipe. When the needle is withdrawn, what prevents the blood from dripping continuously? The answer is interesting, and extremely complex. "The details of the coagulation of blood are very complicated" (Human & Social Biology). The book then states, with engaging simplicity, "It is very important that normal blood in undamaged vessels should not coagulate, and this may be the reason for the complex series of changes that must take place before clotting occurs." So there you are. We don't quite understand how it works, but our lives depend on it. Find the car that does that!

The list goes on. Whatever aspect of the car's design or capability you consider, you will find your own body vastly superior (except for the ability to run at 202 mph — but then, we can go by plane!) This in no way denigrates the value of the car. The much-admired F50 really is worth $500,000. But by looking at this car, and then looking at yourself, your appreciation of the value of a human being is greatly enhanced, and at the same time, so is our appreciation and admiration of the greatness of the One Who created it all.

hinking of traveling to England? How would you like to cross the Atlantic Ocean in a small rubber dinghy? In 1953, Alain Bombard set out from the Canary Islands in a small rubber boat. He wanted to test his theory that shipwrecked people could survive for days at sea. He lived on tiny sea plants and 24 ounces of seawater a day. He reached the West Indies 65 days later, having traveled 2,750 miles. He was 56 pounds thinner, but had proved his point. People eager to stretch the limits of human endurance (see their names in the record books) are prepared to do almost anything. For that reason, the 1,890 miles of salty water that separate the American continent from its British neighbor have been crossed by anything that can float, from raft to rowing boat, from barrel to bathtub. That would be fine if you would be content, as these hardy pioneers were, to live off soggy biscuits and seaweed, but if you would be desirous of a journey in comfort and safety, then a stately liner of the caliber of the QE2 would be your choice of transport.

For people to whom enjoyment in this world is an imperative, and there seem to be many, this is the way to travel. Everything on this boat has been designed for the enjoyment and comfort of the 1,800 or so passengers for their five-day crossing. Consider the following statistics: 7,200 gallons of beer are pumped straight from tankers parked at the wharf into huge stainless steel tanks. Once at sea, 14 bakers start their long day at 5 a.m. preparing the 3,000 or more rolls that will be served at breakfast. The ship boasts 75 all-male chefs — including a special kosher cook in his own kitchen — who are busy all day preparing delicacies for the four dining rooms. People need to drink. The engine room contains a water-purification plant which takes seawater on board and purifies 480 tons for drinking, enough to fill seven swimming pools. The good health of the passengers is of the greatest importance, and, sure enough, the liner is fitted with a hospital, where two doctors, three nurses and three medical attendants can deal with anything from dental work to removing an appendix in the fully equipped operating theater. In case you are worried that a floating hospital can cause seasickness, have no fear. The QE2's hospital is situated midships near the water line, where the movement of the 963-foot-long ship is hardly noticeable. From the queen of ocean liners, you would expect nothing less.

Nor from the ship of the desert. Just like any craft going to sea requires all its provisions before leaving port — there are no service stations at sea — similarly, if you intend to cross the desert, you must be fully equipped before you leave. It can be no fun to have traveled 500 miles into the Sahara Desert only to discover that you left the can opener back

A close-up of the ship of the desert. Notice the hair on the lips and nostrils that close.

home. Is there a craft that has been designed with built-in equipment that can convey passengers safely across the hostile expanses of the sandy desert? Enter the camel.

If you would be asked to draw a caricature of a camel, your picture would certainly include either one hump or two. A hump is to a camel as a trunk is to an elephant. The single-humped variety lives in Africa, and is sometimes called dromedary. Its two-humped cousin lives in Asia, is darker brown in color and its legs are slightly shorter. In the winter, the Asian camel grows its own overcoat of long thick hair which protects it from the bitter cold of the Gobi desert. The ubiquitous hump is the camel's amazing pantry. The comparison between the ship of the desert and the ship of the ocean is not figurative, but absolute! The camel has the ability to store food and water. When the camel eats, it transforms the food into fat, which it stores in its hump. (The hump is not, as many people believe, filled with water. Water is stored in cells all over its body.) During periods when food is scarce, the camel has the ability to change this fat back into food. For this reason, a camel can travel up to 10 days in the hottest weather without drinking, and even longer without eating. However, after such a journey, its larder has been depleted and the hump sags and looks empty. If the QE2 has provisions for 7,130 gallons of water, then the camel does no worse by comparison. When it drinks, it takes up more than 34 gallons at one time. (By contrast, it is difficult for humans to drink two cups of water consecutively without feeling full. We also have an indication of the Matriarch Rebecca's phenomenal kindness in offering to fetch water for Eliezer's ten camels.) After the camel's enormous drink and feed, the hump soon regains its previous size.

Could you imagine crossing over soft ground with tiny pointed heels? The camel is better provided. It has two spreading padded toes on each foot. These flat padded feet are designed for treading on soft sand or hard rocks. (Compare this to the snowshoe hare that owes its name to its huge hind feet which act like snowshoes when it runs and leaps across soft snow. Similarly, the mountain goat can climb incredibly steep slopes, jump from rock to rock, and leap across dangerous ravines. The goat's hooves have sharp edges, which dig into rock crevices, and slightly hollow soles which act like suction pads on the rocky slopes.) The camel might look ungainly, but it has superb balance. In fact it is not customary to allow a riding camel to walk, because the motion is rolling, and you lurch from side to side in a sickly manner. Not for nothing is it called 'the ship of the desert'! A quick jog-trot is the usual gait, and a racing camel can run as fast as 10 miles an hour. It can jump over rocks and travel 90 miles a day, but never does it stumble or fall.

There are many men with beards. Whereas they all have a

healthy growth of hair on their upper lip and on their lower chin, you will never see anyone with hair growing out of his lips. The very fact that the forest growth ends exactly where the lips begin is in itself a remarkable feature of design — imagine the discomfort of bristles at the entrance to your mouth. In fact, you could not imagine any creature that would welcome hair on its lips. Except, of course, the camel. You have to appreciate the camel's diet. It feeds on twigs, shrubs, dry grass and thorny scrub which grow in the sand, and which other animals would not eat. But how will it prevent itself from cutting its mouth on the brambles and thorns? Not a problem. The camel's lips are covered with thick, coarse hairs, which provide it with the perfect protection. It swallows its food quickly, and will bring it up later to chew the cud, just like a cow. But unlike a cow, the camel has a remarkable defense mechanism. When it is angry, it can bring up food from its stomach and spit it at you!

Any ship needs an efficient navigation system, together with special provisions to protect itself in stormy weather, in order to survive a voyage. Our ship of the desert has them all. A camel has exceptionally keen eyesight and sense of smell. Its eyes are set well back into its head, and bushy eyebrows and heavy eyelashes protect them from the adverse elements. Have you, O human being, ever been to the beach when the wind is blowing? Have you ever stood on the wrong side of the towel when it is being shaken out? Does the flying sand irritate your eyes and enter your nose? So why don't you keep your hands by your sides and close your nose! Finding it difficult, are you? It's a shame that you are not a camel. No sand ever penetrates the defenses above its eyes, and it simply closes its nostrils into tight slits during the raging sandstorm. (Closing your nostrils is not as simple as it sounds. It requires an intricate system of muscles, linked to tendons, with its own electrical wiring, all joined to the brain. Desire it? Well, go ahead and develop it!)

When thinking about camels, your mind's eye will paint a picture of Bedouins riding these animals sedately across a sand dune. Their camels gave them much more than a free ride. When the Bedouins were nomads, their camels gave them milk, meat (neither of them kosher), wool, leather and dried manure for fuel. Their womenfolk wove camel hair into cloth. The question, though, is why camels, which are so perfectly designed for life in the desert, should have a woolen coat! Could you imagine wearing a woolen overcoat on a scorching summer day? In fact, the thick fur protects them from the intense heat, keeping them cool during the hot day and warm at night. Even so, camels have an almost unique ability to tolerate wide daily changes in body temperature — sometimes more than 10 degrees Celsius (18 degrees Fahrenheit) between mid-afternoon highs and late-night lows. Since they are large animals, weighing hundreds of pounds, these temperature changes would result in tremendous reduction of water loss, through evaporation that would occur if they regulated their temperature as precisely as other mammals of similar size (they do not need to perspire to reduce their body temperature, because they are perfectly content with a high temperature). Thus they avoid the deadly dehydration that would make life in the desert an impossibility.

Camels are remarkably strong and healthy, considering the poor food they normally eat. It is reported that camels used in desert warfare do not seem much distressed when they are hit by bullets, and recover quickly from wounds. No ship can mend itself! Not only are they equal to any oceangoing vessel, they are in many ways superior. No seagoing ship, from QE2 to row boat, is built without tremendous intelligence. Fortunate is the ship of the desert to have had the greatest Intelligence of all.

A father stood facing his child and repeated his demand. "Will you please go to the store for me?" "With pleasure, Father." But the child did not move. The father was becoming irate. "Son, did you not hear me?" "I heard you perfectly well, Father," answered the son, still rooted to the spot. "Then why do you refuse to go?" "I have not refused, and I do want to go." "Then why are you standing there like a petrified statue?" yelled the father. "Because you are standing on my shoelace, Father!"

There is nothing like cold clinical facts to defuse a potentially explosive situation. And there is nothing like human nature to ignore cold clinical facts. If you are a *Kohen* who participates in *Bircas Kohanim*, you might have met the following situation. The *chazzan* is a wonderful man, who takes his job seriously. While intoning the 15 words of *Birkas Kohanim*, he puts his heart and soul into each word. On occasion, perhaps on *Yom Tov*, he adds luster to his rendering by means of a tune. The *Kohanim* are standing, arms outstretched, as the *chazzan* melodiously but painstakingly meanders through the tune. At some stage, the *Kohanim's* arms begin to ache. The *chazzan*, ignorant of their plight, puts every fiber of effort into extracting every nuance of feeling from the words. The *Kohanim*, in the meantime, are in agony, their arms feel like lead, their muscles beg for relief. Eventually, 'Shalom' is reached, the *chazzan* is delighted by his performance, and the *Kohanim* drop their aching arms with unalloyed pleasure.

Why is it that muscles ache? How long could you hold your arms in a diving position without crying out in agony? Why do *Kohanim* have this problem? Can the problem be solved to enable members of the priestly sect to stretch their arms with equanimity, no matter how lengthy the *chazzan's* rendition?

In attempting to solve the *Kohanim* syndrome, we must first review some quite amazing information about muscles. Muscles are responsible for all the body's movements, from kicking a ball, writing a letter, squeezing digested food through the intestines, to making the heart beat. The body's biggest single muscle is the huge *gluteus maximum*, below your spine, which powers your climbing, running and leaping movements. The smallest muscle is the *stapedius* in the ear, which looks like a tiny piece of thread. Its job is to reduce the vibrations of sound which are too loud!

It is well known that muscles move by contraction. (Interestingly enough, muscle is the only tissue in the body that can do this. All other kinds of tissue — skin, hair, bone, cartilage — stay the same size unless they are growing.) For

Bircas Kohanim is a privilege. But why do Kohanim's arms ache?

example: To raise your hand, the biceps in the front of your upper arm contracts and pulls up the bone of your forearm. To lower your hand, the triceps in the back of your upper arm contracts and straightens the elbow, aided by gravity. Contraction does not change the volume of a muscle, but is rather a result of changes within the muscle fiber. A muscle fiber, which is thinner than a hair, can be up to one foot long in a large muscle. Each muscle fiber is made of a collection of even thinner fibers called *myofibrils*. These consist of long strands of two proteins, *actin* and *myosin*. When the muscle is stimulated (by electrical signals from the brain via the nervous system) the actin pulls the myosin along past it, like a line of people tugging on a rope. This slide-past mechanism makes the myofibril shorten, causing the muscle fiber to contract, and the whole muscle becomes shorter, up to three-fifths of its relaxed length.

It makes you want to smile when you realize the electrochemical wonder involved in smiling! Facial expressions are made by the action of over 40 facial muscles. Many of the muscles of the face are attached, not to bones, but to each other, or to the skin. This remarkable arrangement (read, design) allows us to construct a huge variety of facial expressions that can convey our thoughts, moods and emotions, not to mention eating, speaking and blinking! The ability to register disapproval, happiness, surprise or disgust by using the muscles of your face (you cannot do it with your feet) is nothing more than a miraculous demonstration of muscle power, tailor-made to increase our repertoire of communication.

But that is not all. What is perhaps not as well known is that after receiving the electrical stimulus to move, the muscle requires energy to facilitate the reaction of actin and myosin. That energy must come from somewhere! Along comes the greatest wonder of all. The flight muscles in a housefly and the *tefillin*-wearer's biceps all receive their energy from the same chemical. It is called *adenosine triphosphate*, or ATP. A small amount of ATP exists in all our muscles. When ATP in a muscle combines with water, it breaks down into two parts, ADP (*adenosine diphosphate*) and phosphate. A tiny amount of energy is released, and that energy is used in concert with the reaction of the proteins, actin and myosin, which contracts the muscle. Every time a runner takes a step, a hundred million trillion ATP molecules change to ADP and phosphate. The harder our muscles work, the more ATP they need. (In short, it works like this. Energy from the food you eat is used to combine the chemical ADP with phosphate to produce ATP. Your muscles break down the amazing chemical ATP in order to move. The waste products of this reaction are ADP and phosphate — the very chemicals needed to make more ATP!)

So why do *Kohanim's* arms become tired? If we demand too much from our muscles, ATP cannot be made fast enough. The muscles begin to ache and we become tired. We slow down, even if we don't want to. Our bodies are sending a message: Stop now before all energy is used up!

There is another reason too. Some of our muscles need oxygen to turn food into energy. Other muscles can obtain energy from stored food without the use of oxygen. If you have to escape quickly from a situation of danger, you use the second type of muscle. Food fuel stored in your muscles is immediately used to produce energy. There is no time for your lungs and heart to get oxygen to your leg muscles! But there is a limit to how long these muscles can work without oxygen. When very little oxygen is available to working muscles, a chemical called *lactic acid* is produced. If a lot of lactic acid builds up, it will prevent the muscles from contracting. That is what happens in your legs when you run really fast, or when you stretch your arms out for extended periods. You feel pain and fatigue. That is the reason why sprinters cannot run at full tilt for too long, and why *Kohanim* have to rest their arms.

How can the situation be improved? Again, we learn from the wonders of the human body. You will be pleased to hear that your body is different than a pair of shoes. Shoes wear out with repeated use, but the more you use your body, the better shape it will be in. The best way to build up your muscles is to give them lots of work to do. Weight lifting (or any exercise) actually changes your muscle cells. Muscle cells are long and thin, so they are called fibers. These fibers become thicker with exercise, so that when they contract they can supply more power. If you want to do some basic exercises at home, good old-fashioned push-ups, chin-ups and sit-ups will never let you down. Even if you start with one push-up a day, you will be surprised how quickly you will be doing 10, 20, then 50.

So what is the poor *Kohen* to do if he has no time for exercise? If all else fails, there is one final wonder on which he can rely. When muscles become tired, a nerve called a pain receptor sends signals to the brain that we interpret as pain. Naturally, if we feel too much pain, we stop using the muscle, and it is able to rest. There are, however, chemicals in the brain called *endorphins* which can control the information the brain receives from pain receptors. During a long run like a marathon, the brain increases the amount of endorphins it produces. This reduces the effect of the signals from the pain receptors in the muscles, and runners feel the results as a gradual disappearing of the pain that has been building up during their run. Many runners experience a feeling of happiness as the pain diminishes, and they receive an extra burst of energy to keep going. This is probably one of the reason that marathoners can run such long distances. And why *Kohanim* can continue to hold their hands high, praising the Great Intelligence of this fantastic machine, and bless His people.

There is no doubt whatsoever that if your great-grandfather, who lived 100 years ago, would accompany you to a *chasunah* in these modern times, he would be amazed. It would not be the food that would surprise him; after all, people have always eaten. The band would not shock him, although in truth he would find it difficult to accept the level of noise, and you might find it problematic explaining the labyrinth of wires emanating from the electronic keyboard. Pianos have been around for a long time, and the keyboard does bear some resemblance to the traditional instrument. What he would find most astonishing would be something entirely different. Very often at weddings (and many other locations too), you are sitting next to someone when suddenly you hear a soft ringing. Your neighbor places his hand into his jacket pocket, and pulls out a small piece of plastic. Placing the plastic into the palm of his hand, with one end held to his ear and the other close to his mouth, he begins speaking. Particularly at weddings, you see people walk across the floor, oblivious to everyone else, talking into these diminutive pieces of plastic with great enthusiasm.

Naturally, your great-grandfather would be intrigued. What on earth is he doing? Why is he talking to himself, holding a piece of plastic? So tell him. Tell him that the man is not talking to himself. If the wedding is in America, tell him that he is talking to one of his relatives in *Eretz Yisrael*. If the wedding is in *Eretz Yisrael*, explain to your great-grandfather that his relative is in New York, and he too is holding a piece of plastic, and that they are deep in conversation. Would he believe you? As he is trying to recover from shock, inform him that with this little piece of plastic, which you keep in your inside pocket, you can talk to anyone anywhere in the world! The venerable gentleman, who is accustomed to intercontinental communication taking months, would simply not be able to accept what you are saying. It would be the wonder of wonders to beat all wonders. It would be like explaining that by holding your teacup to your mouth you could talk to someone across the ocean. How could he possibly accept that? The truth is, however, that even for our own sophisticated generation, we are equally amazed at the phenomenon of the cellular. We use it, we benefit from it, we pay for it — but we never cease to be amazed by it. It is good to be amazed, but it is also important to realize that the very same physical principles that make the telephone our very best friend (or worst enemy) are mirrored precisely in our own bodies. If the innovation of cellular telephones staggers your imagination, then let the wonders of your own body take your breath away!

It sounds simple enough. Sound waves from your voice vibrate a thin metal diaphragm in the cellular telephone

Carry on, smiling young man — speaking to someone 3,000 miles away
through a piece of plastic is fantastic!

handset, and they are converted into radio waves. These radio waves are then directed (via computer) to the earpiece of the receiving telephone and they are converted back to sound waves, which are recognized as speech. In practice, however, it is anything but simple. The conversion of sound waves into radio waves involves transforming energy waves of very low frequency (sound) into energy waves of extremely high frequency (radio), or superimposing the sound waves onto the radio waves, which, as you can imagine, is complex.

That's fine. But have you ever thought what exactly sound is? Let us imagine that you pluck a tight rubber band. The rubber band begins to vibrate. This in turn disturbs the air around it. These disturbances in the air make a sound wave. How does sound travel through air? A sound wave is started by something moving (the vibrating rubber band). The moving object pushes the particles of the substances, which could be air, around it. These pushed particles then pass on the energy to the next particles, and so on. In that way, sound travels by one moving particle causing its neighboring particles to move. Sound can travel through any substance — solid, liquid or gas. Substances are made up of particles, which can be moved as described above. In gas (and air is transparent gas), the particles are far apart, and the speed of sound is slow, because much of the energy of the moving object that makes the sound is lost in pushing the gas particles until they meet other particles. For that reason sound travels five times faster through water and 25 times faster through steel than it does through the air. It also explains why in outer space there is no sound, for in space there is no air, thus there is nothing to pass on sound vibrations. Rockets, which are so noisy on earth that they can deafen, are completely silent in space. There is no air to carry their sound.

If you are looking for design in the human body, it is sufficient to observe that having the ability to produce meaningful sound (speech) would be of no value whatsoever if the person to whom you were directing those sounds had no ability to receive and comprehend them. It would be exactly like speaking into a telephone to someone who does not possess a telephone! Thus, the vocal cords presuppose a sound-receiving mechanism (ears), and our ears declare that people can produce sound. The human body, like everything in the created world, is a completely coordinated structure. The Creator of the body knew that sound can travel through air, and so there is speech!

It is well known that the human ear can be divided into three sections, the outer, the middle and the inner ear. Listen to some of its special features. The outer ear (sometimes called the pinna) is supported by cartilage which has extra elastic fiber to give it additional flexibility. It is precisely shaped to direct moving sound particles into the earhole. The walls of the tunnel leading down to the eardrum contain wax glands, to protect the eardrum and to keep it pliable. The wax is prevented from clogging the ear by special hairs, which also deter dust and insects from entering the tunnel.

The eardrum, which is stretched tightly across the width of the tunnel, is no ordinary skin. It is a membrane which contains many fibers of different lengths so that it vibrates equally to sound waves of different frequencies. Accidental? The eardrum vibrates, just like a drum, when you hear sounds. There must be air on both sides of the eardrum for it to vibrate. What is the source of the air on the inside of your eardrum? After all, it is inside your head! Fortunately, the air comes up from your throat through a narrow tube (the Eustachian tube) to your inner ear. Were it not for the Eustachian tube, which equalizes air pressure on either side of the eardrum, flying in a plane, where the air pressure can change rapidly, would be an excruciating, if not highly dangerous, activity. Three tiny bones (the smallest in your body, and the only ones that never grow) help the sound travel from the eardrum to the inner ear. They rock in a lever-like manner, which increases the power of the vibrations, and they are held tightly together by muscles, so that there is no sound loss. We have learned that sound can travel through soft material (one moving particle causing its neighbor to move . . .) and since bone is very dense, the sound conduction through the three tiny bones is fast and efficient. The Designer of the ears knew all that!

Then comes the greatest wonder of all. Somehow, vibrating sound waves have to be converted into electrical impulses and sent to the brain to be interpreted into meaningful sound, and then stored in the memory bank. This is where the ear and the telephone converge. The three bones transfer the vibrations to a small membrane — the oval window, which is set in the inner ear. The inner ear consists of a labyrinth made of membrane, which is set in a bony labyrinth of the same shape. The sensitive mechanism is very well protected! This labyrinth is coiled, snail shaped, and is called the cochlea. It contains three separate channels, all filled with liquid. As the vibrations ripple through the fluid in the three chambers, they shake a delicate membrane that runs along its whole length. You will be pleased to know that this membrane contains up to 30,000 fibers which vary in length, thickness and tension. Each fiber resonates to vibrations of a particular wavelength, so that a different section of the membrane reacts to a different pitch of sound. Attached to that membrane are microscopic hairs, which in turn are embedded in hair cells. When the membrane shakes, it pulls the hairs, causing the hair cells to produce the electrical signal that travels along the auditory nerve to the brain. The sound is then stored in the memory. Is it a 30-number memory, like your modern telephone? Not quite; your personal memory is limitless, capable of storing millions of sounds, and able to recall any one of those millions of sounds from the memory bank, instantly.

We can learn a great deal from your great-grandfather. The stimulated excitement that he would demonstrate when observing the cellular phone-users for the first time is an excitement which we would do well to emulate . . . and then understand that the greatest excitement of all ought to be reserved for that everyday ability — the ability that we have always had to transmit and receive sound. For it is that ability that so eloquently proclaims the fathomless wisdom of the Creator of all things.

The Great Drain

This is a true story — not too dramatic, but true nevertheless. The summer had been exceptionally hot, and there had been no rain, not even a shower, for many weeks. And this in a country (England) where they say that the only difference between summer and winter is that in summer the rain is warmer! Things were so serious that an official drought was declared, a ban on watering the lawns was announced, and the Jewish community proclaimed a *Yom Tefillah*. It was more effective than anyone would have dared to believe! Not too long afterwards, the rains began. It commenced with light showers, and quickly developed into more prolonged rain. Then came the day of the deluge.

The clouds were low and dark. The air hung heavy with suspense. The drops of rain that began spasmodically, splattered against the pavement — and then the skies opened. It was as if the heavens had become a gigantic hose, switched on at full force, aimed at the earth. Torrents of water hammered down from the sky, and for more than one hour, the rain fell with monsoon consistency, making it impossible to venture out for more than one second without becoming drenched. The world had turned to water — water gushing along the ground, pouring off roofs, cascading over gutters.

One particular street was built on the side of a hill. At the bottom of the hill stood a row of houses, meeting the sloping road face on. At the height of the storm, the sloping road was transformed into a veritable river, with water pouring towards the dwellings at the foot of the hill. No problem really, for there were drains in front of the houses to catch any rain water. On this particular day, the drains were blocked. The water, which respects neither personality nor property, poured over the drain, straight under the door of the nearest house, wreaking damp and watery havoc. It was not until someone was courageous enough to brave the downpour and clear the drain that the river was rerouted, and a semblance of normality restored.

Like so many things of value, we take drains completely for granted, and we begin to appreciate them (and perhaps for the first time notice their existence) when they are blocked! Indeed, there are places where no drainage system exists, and the winter rains make the roads impassable. No one has yet devised a system whereby you can plant a drain, grow a drain or wish one into existence. They are either planned and built, at great expense, as part of a comprehensive system, or you manage as best as you can without them. Conversely, if you benefit from a drainage system that operates efficiently, you will be happy to accredit praise and compliments to the designer of that which makes life so pleasurable.

That being the case, have a look at yourself! Built into every human is a drainage system so efficient and so sophisticated that it makes the drainage system down there in the street as archaic as a bicycle with a wooden wheel. What is it all about?

One of the facts concerning the human body which never ceases to amaze people, and indeed is practically impossible to register in the mind, is that if all the veins and capillaries that transport blood in an individual would be laid end to end, they would encircle the world twice. We are talking about a distance of approximately 72,000 miles! This enormous transport network (larger than the transport system of many countries) provides the nourishment and removes the waste from every single cell in the body, apart from certain isolated locations which have their own nutritional arrangements. But did you know that in between each cell there is a space? What is there in that space?

It works as follows. Blood is contained in a closed system of vessels and is kept circulating by the heart. One of the constituent ingredients of the blood is a substance called plasma. Plasma is colorless and consists mainly of water, but has many important substances dissolved in it. They include salts and food substances such as glucose. Plasma also contains an important group of substances called plasma proteins. There are three types of plasma protein, and each has an important job to do. The first is *albumen* (the same protein found in the white of an egg), and this makes the blood thick and viscous. The second is *globulin*, and is vital for destroying germs. The third is *fibrinogen*, and this protein plays an important part in the clotting of blood. As the blood circulates, some of the fluid, the plasma, escapes from the capillaries by a system called diffusion (a separate wonder of its own) and surrounds each cell, providing it with nourishment and removing any waste product. Once the plasma has left the capillary, it changes its name. No longer shall your name be called plasma, but you shall be known as tissue fluid.

Now there is a problem. It may be relatively simple to leave a moving vehicle; it is quite another matter to rejoin it. Similarly, it is one thing for the plasma to leave the mighty transportation system of the blood supply, but quite another for the tissue fluid to be readmitted. Enter the drainage system!

Quite apart from the 72,000 miles of blood supply, our bodies are permeated by narrow channels called *lymph vessels*. The lymph vessels provide an entirely independent transport system which has been designed to facilitate the safe return of tissue fluid to the heart. At first tiny, with very thin walls, these lymph vessels join up to form larger vessels, which eventually unite into two main ducts, and empty their contents into the large veins entering the heart.

There are two amazing features of the lymphatic system which no drainage system anywhere in the world possesses. The lymph flow takes place in one direction only, from the tissues to the heart. Could you possibly suggest how to induce the liquid in the lymph to travel uphill? Remember that in the lymphatic system, as opposed to the blood supply, there is no specialized pumping organ! The flow is caused partly by the pressure of the fluid which accumulates in the vessels, but one of the most important factors in the movement of the fluid is muscular exercise. This is a drainage system operated by muscle power! Occasionally tissue fluid is formed faster than it can be drained away in the vessels, especially when there is insufficient muscular action, and swelling can be caused. But even where there is muscular action to assert pressure on the lymph vessels, compressing them and causing the fluid to flow, what will guarantee that the fluid flows in the right direction, and how will we prevent backflow? The answer is an amazing system of valves which run the length of the lymphatic system. There is nothing that demonstrates the existence of wisdom more than a valve. Every car and bicycle tire relies on its valve to ensure that air flows in one direction only. The valve is forced open by the pressure of the air (or the fluid in our lymphatic system), but if that pressure becomes less, the backward pressure from beyond the valve closes the valve against its seat, preventing a return flow. Just like the car, and the bike, so in you. Fantastic!

The second feature of the lymphatic system is perhaps even more breathtaking. Could you imagine that on its way through the drainage system, the water that flows is purified of all impurities, emerging crystal clear at the far end? That and no less is what happens with us. On its way through the lymph vessels to the ducts, the lymph (tissue fluid) passes through a number of lymph glands. These are little swellings at intervals along the length of the lymph vessels. Each lymph gland is full of tiny spaces like a sponge, and the lymph has to filter through these spaces, which are filled with a network of fibers, before it can continue on its journey back to the bloodstream. Attached to these fibers are white cells which can trap and consume foreign particles in the lymph fluid. The lymph fluid passing through a gland is thus filtered of any invading bacteria before it is returned to the circulation.

What remarkable design! Here we have a drainage system that not only is invaluable in the circulation of our blood and supply of nutrients to our cells, but a drainage system that incorporates courageous defenders to help fight disease. Some of the defenders actually eat up the germs (these are called *phagocytes*), while others produce antibodies against them. The main lymph glands are located in the neck, under the arms and in the groin. Occasionally, if there is an infection, the germs get trapped in the nearby lymph gland, where the specialized cells try their best to prevent them from entering the rest of the body. This might cause the gland to swell and become tender and painful. When Mother feels the swollen glands at the neck, she knows that Junior has a throat infection. This means that the lymph glands are valiantly performing their remarkably specialized task.

Go into the street and think. Is there a drain anywhere in the civilized world that can compete with our own drainage system? It is not really a competition. Even a crude aperture in the ground, with a rough iron grating cover, would be ample evidence of intelligence. How much more the dazzlingly sophisticated system that we find within ourselves. Sometimes it needs a rainy day to be made aware of the wonders that abound within our own bodies.

בָּרוּךְ אַתָּה ה' . . . רוֹפֵא כָל בָּשָׂר וּמַפְלִיא לַעֲשׂוֹת

Blessed are You, Hashem . . .
Who heals all flesh and acts wondrously.

The Peashooter

Probably you would never admit to it. After all, in your exalted position, at your time of life, you might find it just a little embarrassing. When you were young, did you — or if you are still young, do you — use a peashooter? There is nothing like it. For stealth and effectiveness, it is unbeatable. While the teacher is writing on the board (keep this part secret; otherwise all teachers will stop using the board) you put a dried hard bean in your mouth, place the trusty metal pipe to your mouth, take aim at a friend who can take a joke, and fire. In the time it takes for your friend to let out an outraged cry, and for the teacher to whirl around to discover the cause of the disturbance, the pipe can be back in your pocket with an angelic look bathing your countenance. Alternative methods of registering your presence in a class, or declaring your affection to your friends, such as placing a straight pin on their chair, or squirting them with a water gun, can cause pain and dampness, and should always be avoided. Tricks such as balancing a bowl of water over a half-opened door are also ineffective, as experience has shown that invariably the wrong person opens the door, or the bowl tips over behind the door, and in any event is such a waste of precious water, that it should not even be mentioned.

The list of practical jokes is endless, and most of them are harmless. People whose motives are less benign have utilized great ingenuity in making their point felt by their adversaries. In the famous series of wars between England and France known as the Hundred Years' War which lasted from 1337 to 1453, the French developed the use of the crossbow. This machine was aimed like a rifle, and when the trigger was released, shot a short bolt at such great force that it could pierce the chain mail of their enemies at a range of 1,200 feet. However, the English archers won many of the battles because they used the longbow, which required greater physical force, shot arrows further than the bolts of the French, and could be fired at greater speed. Things have developed since then. The Chinese are generally accredited for inventing gunpowder, which contains saltpeter, charcoal and sulphur, and is ignited by the application of a flame or heat. By the late 1400s, muskets which could fire metal projectiles were being used on battlefields, and cannons were destroying the thick-walled castles which until then were virtually invincible. In America, the year 1884 saw Mr. H. Maxim patenting his fully automatic machine gun. The force of the recoil when the gun was fired recocked it, so that it continued to fire automatically. If you want to come really up to date, then you will be pleased to know that the American GE Vulcan machine gun can fire 6,000 bullets in a single minute!

The one thing that all weapons have in common, from the simple and relatively harmless peashooter to the most sophisticated tank, is intelligence. That means that although they have no intelligence of their own, they all demonstrate intellect and design. You could say that the more complex the weapon, the greater the intellect and intelligence that must have been invested in its construction. One thing is clear. No human being has weapons built into his body. If you want a peashooter you have to go and get one. If you want an anti-ballistic missile launcher, there is simply no alternative to going to your local supermarket and buying one. You can neither grow one, nor expect to find one in between your fingers. What then would you say to a living creature that grows with an integral weapon system? Not only that, but it can lay eggs that eventually produce other living creatures that have precisely that same weapon system. Would that not demonstrate intelligence in its design?

Sitting in your *succah* basking in the subtle ambience of the *Yom Tov* atmosphere, all is peace and serenity. In flies a bee. Panic! There is little use trying to quell the rising tension by releasing information that if you leave bees alone they won't harm you, or quoting statistics such as the boy who was stung 2,243 times by an angry swarm and survived (true!), for those who are scared are scared, and with good reason. A honeybee has been created with a lance in its tail. This lance is not straight, but barbed. When the bee pushes the sting into its victim's skin, it gets stuck. The sting and sac which contains the poison are ripped off the honeybee as it departs, pumping poison while the bee goes off to die. More than fifty different chemicals have been identified from various species of ants, bees and wasps. They all inject poison either in defense (in the case of the bees) or to paralyze prey. Some cause itching, pain, swelling and redness, others destroy cells and spread the poison. One particularly delightful species of wasp is the sand wasp, which paralyzes a caterpillar with nerve poison. The immobile caterpillar is then stored as food for the young wasps. Now tell them to 'just keep still!'

The next time you are in Malaysia, do be careful. In that far-off country lives an innocent-looking moth that has the ability to pierce the hide of tapirs, buffaloes and other mammals. The hide of these large animals is by no means thin, but the vampire moth — for such is its name — is able to utilize its long proboscis (a hollow tube emanating from its mouth) to suck blood for up to an hour. The proboscis is constructed in two halves. Rapid side-to-side bending drives one tip, then the other, against the skin, finally breaking through. Then it begins to drill. Fast rocking of the head straightens the proboscis and drives it into the animal, while the blood pressure from the unsuspecting animal erects barbs on the proboscis that grip the flesh. Not so pleasant to think about (especially if you are a buffalo), but it does demonstrate an absolute masterpiece of engineering.

Think for a moment what specialist knowledge is required by the not-so-friendly bee. It must know what poison is harmful to potential enemies, humans included. This information is important, for were the substance beneficial, like the honey that it also produces so successfully, then it would achieve the opposite effect. It must be able to produce a pointed sting, as thin as a pin, yet strong enough to penetrate the skin barrier of its adversaries. Now comes the difficult part. This pin-thin sting must be hollow, in order to allow free passage of the poison. The bee must have a pumping mechanism to convey the poisonous liquid into its enemy, without which the poison would remain impotently in its own abdomen. It goes without saying that the bee must be capable of developing and producing a system whereby it can safely store a deadly poison within its own body, without any detrimental effect to itself. All that is quite a lot to ask of a bee, especially when you realize that every part of the mechanism must operate simultaneously for it to work at all. Half a system is useless, any attempt to develop a poison before you have the applicator or the built-in immunity is suicidal; and you will appreciate that it is very difficult to develop an immunity to a poison that does not yet exist. Everything must have been present at once, and at the beginning. A phenomenally complex weapon cannot produce itself. A weapon has an inventor, and a bee has a Creator.

It is not only on land that you will find impressive weaponry, but also at sea. Students of history might know that after the Romans invaded the British Isles in the year 43, Queen Boudicca led an uprising against the tyrannical Roman governor in the year 61. In history books, she is depicted waving a sword while riding a chariot which had blades set at right angles into the axle of the wheels. This created some discomfort to any Roman soldiers who happened to come too close. It is amazing to know that in the coral reefs of the tropical Pacific, swims an innocent-looking fish — with a sinister-sounding name, surgeonfish — which has an uncanny resemblance to Queen Boudicca's chariot. The name 'surgeon' comes from a sharp, bony, blade-like 'lancet' on either side of the body, near the base of the tail. These blades cut flesh as cleanly as a surgeon's scalpel. The lancet lies folded in a groove when not in use, but is flicked out at right angles to the fish for use when the fish suddenly turns and thrashes its tail at its enemy. It is important to know that the surgeonfish is the only species with this particular weapon. If the knife in the tail is such a successful weapon, why does every fish not have one? For that matter, why don't you have a couple of knives sticking out of your ankles? Other fish seem to survive very happily without a set of cutlery tucked away in their tail. The answer? This particular fish was created with this weapon, others were not.

If you want to identify the fish whose armor most closely resembles the schoolboy's peashooter, then the archerfish is your candidate. This fish is able to catch food which is entirely out of the water. When hungry, it can squirt a jet of water at insects and other creatures on leaves and stems above the water. The surprise attack knocks the prey into the water, where the archerfish snaps it up. Again, special construction and design in the fish is essential. When the archerfish is ready to shoot, it snaps shut its gill covers, thereby compressing water in the gills and in the mouth. Its tongue presses upwards against a special groove in the roof of the mouth, acting like a valve to keep the water under pressure, and turning the groove into a tube which produces a fast, narrow stream of water.

The watery peashooter, in common with every insect and fish which has been created with its own unique, effective and specialized weaponry, demonstrates a degree of design and intelligence unsurpassed in the manufactured world. Nothing can create itself. Design and intelligence all point to the Supreme Designer who created the world.

בָּרוּךְ שֶׁאָמַר וְהָיָה הָעוֹלָם

Blessed is He Who spoke, and the world came into being.

The Channel Tunnel

Between England and France lies a stretch of water known as the English Channel. At its narrowest point it is only 21 miles and until recently crossing it was a slow and uncomfortable business. Julius Caesar crossed the channel in 54 B.C.E. The Normans landed in their turn in the 11th century, led by William the Conqueror, and both Napoleon and more recent despots have tried to invade the indomitable island. Linking Britain to the continent became an obsession in the 19th century. Plan after plan was suggested, from the craziest to the most inspired: conveyor belts, sunken or floating tubes, tunnels, dikes, bridges and ferries. A French engineer, Monsier de Gamond, is considered the 'father' of the Channel Tunnel. He spent all his money and energy planning a fixed cross-Channel link. He had various ideas, but finally decided on an underground railway tunnel with a very similar route to today's tunnel. To study the sea floor, he made dangerous underwater dives. He weighted his body with bags of pebbles, and filled his ears and nostrils with buttered cotton to protect himself from the water pressure! In 1867 he won the support of Queen Victoria of Britain, 'in her own name and in the name of all those ladies who suffer from seasickness'!

All the plans came to nothing. It wasn't until Prime Minister Margaret Thatcher came on the scene that an Anglo-French treaty was officially approved on July 29th, 1987 between herself and President Francois Mitterrand, and work on the huge tunnel could finally begin. As can be imagined, the problems involved in digging almost 100 miles of tunnel were enormous. Among the lesser problems were how to dispose of 2,400 tons of clay each hour (there is a limit to how many garbage bags you can put out for pick-up), how to make three tunnels immune to leaks and earthquakes, and how to coordinate the supplies for the total of more than 7,000 English and French workers who were employed on the site. Without doubt, however, the greatest problem was the simplest one. When two sides are drilling from opposite ends, how do you keep on course? Even the slightest deviation — a fraction of one degree — would have meant that the British and French tunnels did not meet under the middle of the English Channel. That would have been just a bit embarrassing. The problem is that once underground, it is not easy to tell exactly where you are. Even the latest satellite guidance systems are no use.

The only way to keep on course was to survey down the tunnel to work out where they were. The tunnel engineers did so with incredible accuracy, using laser beams. The onboard computer in the cabin reacted to the laser beam, and plotted the tunnel boring machine (TBM)'s exact position.

The operator could then adjust the hydraulic rams behind the cutting head to drive the TBM forward on exactly the right course. They managed. On December 1, 1990, just three years to the day after work had commenced, two workmen, Philippe Cozetter from France and Graham Fagg from England, cut away the last piece of blue clay, and exchanged a historic handshake.

You don't have to be English, or even French, to appreciate what an achievement the Channel Tunnel was, not only politically, but more importantly, technically. It is considered Europe's most amazing engineering achievement, and the fact that they did manage to meet in the middle is perhaps the detail that deserves the greatest attention and maximum praise. It is almost an insult to the intelligence to state that the fact that the two sides met precisely on target was no accident, but the result of technology and planning of the most advanced degree. It's simply too obvious.

Would you like to hear something even more amazing? Take a look at the human brain. The average brain has about 30 billion nerve cells. Each nerve cell sprouts between 10,000 to 100,000 fibers in order to contact other nerve cells in the brain. Taken together, the number of these connections is approximately 10 trillion. Numbers of this magnitude are difficult to imagine, but there they are. Despite all these connections, this forest of fibers is not a chaotic, random tangle, but actually a highly organized network, where most fibers have specific communication functions, and follow regular pathways through the brain. It has been calculated that if only 100th of the brain's connections were specifically routed, that would still add up to more connections than in the Earth's entire communications network.

This type of information has to be allowed to sink in. The fact is that within our brain, we have 10 trillion connections. A complete schematic diagram of this network would stagger the imagination. All the telephone cables in the world would comprise nothing more than a small fraction of it. Now comes the amazing part. The nerve cells of the brain are called neurons. The neurons, like all other cells, contain a nucleus, in

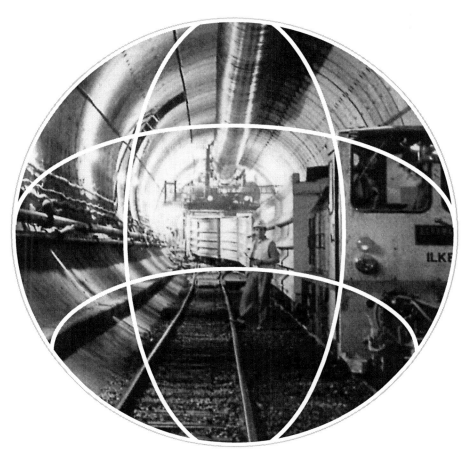

Amazing technology — but how did they meet in the middle?

which lie a catalogue of instructions inherited from father and mother. Every single interconnection must be spelled out in the catalogue. Do you see the problem? As the brain develops in the embryo, 10 billion nerve cells have to connect with each other. Some individual nerve cells have not just one connection, but up to 100,000 connections. That's a lot. How do they actually meet up and connect with each other? Do they just reach out for each other haphazardly? Obviously not, since all neurons fulfill definite, specialized functions, not random ones. Connections between the nerves associated with hearing and those controlling, for example, the bicep muscles, would neither be effective nor logical, for the nervous system coordinates all our movements. If the brain would contain just two nerve cells, which managed to locate each other and form a connection in the developing child, that in itself would be a wonder comparable to Monsieur Cozetter and Mr. Fagg meeting under the English Channel. But the brain contains many more than two nerve cells. The number of connections in the brain is many times more than all the telephones in the world. And somehow, all the correct connections are made, with unswerving accuracy. The design which is apparent in the normal development of a baby is so breathtaking that we remain bewildered by its complexity. It is only when we see a much simpler example — the Channel Tunnel — that we can begin to appreciate what is involved.

The photograph of the two diggers exchanging flags depicts happiness and justifiable pride. Their countries, and the thousands of workers involved, had, after all, achieved something remarkable. It was a breakthrough, literally and technologically. In other places in the world, however, with much less fanfare and publicity, there are wonders taking place regularly which cause the Channel achievement to pale into relative insignificance. Consider the salmon. This regal fish lays its eggs inland, usually far up some freshwater stream. During its second year, the young salmon moves downstream to the sea. When it reaches maturity, it heads back towards its birthplace to spawn (lay its own eggs). This might happen after an interval of up to five years. The salmon swims steadily, advancing three to ten miles a day, always against the current. It can drive up through the swiftest rapids. It can surmount a 10-foot sheer waterfall, making it in one mighty leap. To reach the small pool where it was hatched, it has to make choices at fork after fork of the waterways. How does the salmon find its way back through hundreds, perhaps thousands, of miles of trackless ocean to the same river and same gravel bed where it was hatched? No satisfying explanation has ever been given. It has been suggested that perhaps it uses subtle sensory cues — perhaps the chemical sensitivity to its birthplace so keen that it can detect even slight traces of it intermingled in other waters. But no one really knows for sure. Here is a homing instinct so powerful that it never errs, yet so complex that it cannot be understood by man.

A green turtle returns to the sea after having laid her eggs in the sand. When baby green turtles hatch from their eggs, they must do two things: Dig upward through the sand in which the mother deposited the eggs; then head for the water. To guide them for the first action, they have a built-in urge to go uphill. But then, as a rule, they must go downhill to find water. What cancels instruction 1 and supplies instruction 2? Again it has been suggested that the answer might be light. Water reflects the light from the sky, and it flashes the baby turtles a signal that overrides their uphill orders. Any different than the laser beam that guided the giant cutting machines under the Channel?

The amazing behavior of the Atlantic eels is unique. Eels spend many years of seemingly contented life in the ponds and streams of Europe and North America. Suddenly, they leave their homes, go down the rivers and head out into the Atlantic until they reach a great deep in the Altantic Ocean south of Bermuda, where they sink and disappear forever. Later an eruption of tiny, transparent, threadlike creatures comes welling up to the surface, spreading out like an ever-expanding mushroom. The baby eels miraculously sort themselves out and take the right current to the right continent (no one has ever reported an American eel in Europe, or a European eel in America). Both shoals — by now grown into young eels — swim up the rivers of their respective continents until they reach the precise abodes from where their parents started out.

No one knows how, but happen it does. The lesson is always the same. Whether it is the neurons in the brain, the salmon, the turtles or the eels, we suddenly are made aware that lasers, sonar and computers are primitive instruments compared to the brilliance and complexity of that which exists in the created world. If the Channel Tunnel is a masterpiece of human design, how would you describe the level of design so clearly manifested in Hashem *Yisbarach's* wonderful world?

The Eyes Have It

here is no doubt about it, it happens to be true. The changes are tremendous, and all are known by you. You don't have to be ancient to remember cars without heaters. People dressed up with various layers of clothing to insulate themselves against the biting unrelenting cold that made a car journey in the winter something like a vacation in a refrigerator. Similarly, you do not have to be as old as Methuselah to remember that in the ancient days, cars did not possess tape recorders. In those far-off days, if you wanted to hear a *devar Torah*, you actually had to say one, and if you wanted to hear music you had no choice but to sing. Life was unbelievably difficult in earlier times! But even that was better than the original car — invented by Karl Benz of Germany in 1885 — which was completely open to the elements, and looked very much like a park bench perched above two enormous wheels, which in turn were powered by a gasoline engine which transmitted power to the wheels by a leather belt. The braking system then was not quite the advanced braking system much favored by modern vehicles, more likely a heavy iron anchor attached to a rope which you threw out when you wanted to stop. Benz's friend Gottlieb Daimler, also a native of Germany, did improve things by 1887. He built the very first four-wheeled car, but it still looked like a carriage with an engine instead of a horse!

Go into a car now, and Benz or Daimler would not recognize it. Give a little squeeze to your ignition key, and the car doors open for you, while the lights wink a smiling welcome to their devoted driver. You want to avoid the horrors of a cold seat? No problem, sir; just set your seat warmer to the desired temperature and sit back and relax in cosseted comfort. And have you heard the latest? (If your car does not possess this innovative refinement, you will just have to change your car.) At the side of the steering wheel there is a little stick. Press the button, and a voice speaks to you! It says, "Welcome — the vehicle's computer is now checking systems for you." It really does! Whether there is a little man hidden away in the glove compartment who has been trained to give his lecture has not yet been discovered, but there is a diminutive screen on which invaluable information is displayed, courtesy of the computer. It takes into consideration the average fuel consumption, and tells you how many miles you have left with the remaining fuel. It's marvelous — you now no longer have to sit in a state of advanced nervousness as you see the fuel-gauge needle hovering around the empty mark, wondering if you will be stranded in the midst of nowhere overnight. Ah, the joys of modern technology!

And oh, the joys of ancient technology! Do you see what I mean? In that case you will agree that the eyes possess a degree of sophistication which is breathtaking in its complexity. Most people know that our eye works like a small camera. There is a film at the back of the camera on which the picture is made. Your eye has a kind of film at the back called a *retina*. The retina is made up of millions of tiny nerve cells called rods and cones. The rods respond to dim light for seeing at night, and the cones react to bright light and colors. There are three types of cone cells in the retina. Each type is sensitive to only one color, either red, green or blue. When a colored ray of light reaches the retina and 'fires' the nerve cells, the three types of cone cells break the light into the three primary colors. By mixing red, blue and green light in different ways, we can make any other color. Scientists are still not sure how the brain 'sees' a colored picture. Each cone may deal with one small part of the view the eye sees. Small groups of cones send their messages to a special cell, called the bipolar cell. The signals from these cones are then sent as a 'collected' message to the brain along the optic nerve. The brain translates the signals from the bipolar cells and uses them to build up a colored picture of the original view. It all works like a jigsaw puzzle. Each bipolar cell unit will receive signals from only one piece of the retina. The brain then takes these pieces and puts them all together again to build up a colored picture. Impressed?

There is even more. The human retina has approximately 120 million rods, and 7 million cones. On the other hand, there are less than one million nerve fibers in the optic nerve. Somehow those 127 million rods and cones have to link up to one million nerve fibers. This is done by a complex arrangement of relay nerve cells and synapses resulting in a great deal of data reduction in the retina. The significance of these interconnections has only recently been discovered. This network of nerve interconnections performs the function of image enhancement. The image formed on the retina is blurred, but, by means of carefully arranged interconnections, much of the blur is eliminated by the nerve interactions, in a manner similar to the way images received from spaceships are processed. Did you ever think sight was simple?

Many owls can see in surroundings that are one hundred times darker than human vision can penetrate

If you want to know something of the sophistication in the design of eyes, listen to something amazing. Have you ever been out on a dark night, and noticed a cat's eyes shining in the dark? Motorists sometimes pick up a pair of shining eyes in the beam of their car headlights when driving along a lonely road at night. What is that shine? Seeing at night is difficult, as there is not very much light about. All nocturnal animals have more rods (for seeing in dim light) than cones (which detect color) on the sensitive retina at the back of their eyes. This allows them to see better in dim light. But that is not all. Light enters the eye and passes through to the retina at the back. Here it fires off impulses in the sensitive rods. However, not all of the light stimulates the retina the first time around. Nocturnal animals have a reflecting mirror, called the *tapetum*, behind the retina. This helps them to reuse any light passing through. It gives the light a second chance to act on the retina by bouncing it back towards the nerve cells. Animals with a tapetum see twice as well in the dark as those without one! The reflecting eyes are in reality the tiny guanine crystals that formulate the mirrorlike layer of tapetum.

Can you see in pitch black? It depends if you have been provided with very special sense organs. Some snakes, including vipers and boas, are able to catch their prey even on the darkest nights. They do this by picking up infrared signals from warm objects, including small mammals. As well as their ordinary eyes, which are used in the normal way, these snakes have a second pair of heat-seeking eyes, called pit organs. They provide the snake with a complete heat picture of the area around it. A rattlesnake's pit organs are the most sensitive heat receptors known in the world. Each pit (located just beneath its cold, cruel eyes) contains a thin membrane behind which is an air-filled space. This membrane contains about 100,000 times more nerve endings than humans have on the same area of skin. Each nerve ending responds to infrared heat coming from warm objects in the snake's surroundings. By using these heat-detecting 'eyes,' a rattlesnake can ambush a mouse in the dark as easily as a grass snake captures a frog in the daytime. Something of the efficiency of the heat pits can be gauged by the fact that the snake can sense a temperature difference between two objects of 100th of a single degree. (By contrast, the car's computer will tell you the outside temperature within a two-degree accuracy.)

Picture an owl, and what do you think of? Large staring eyes and a fierce expression. An owl is the expert of the animal world when it comes to night hunting. No animal can see in complete darkness, but an owl can make do with the least amount of light possible. A barn owl can catch a mouse in conditions that humans would consider 'pitch black.' Many owls can see in surroundings that are 100 times darker than human vision can penetrate. How does an owl do it? First of all, its eyes have many more rods than cones, enabling it to see in the dimmest of light. Its eyes are enormous, with huge pupils, and fantastic binocular vision. Its eyes are so big that they take up most of the front of the skull. Most animals are able to move their eyes using the special muscles attached to their eyes. (You probably know that your very own eyes are moved by muscles — you are now using them to scan the lines of this book!) However, the owl has a problem. There is no room to fit any muscles in its eye orbit! The bony wall that lies between the orbits is so thin that the eyes almost touch. So, instead of moving its eyes, the owl moves its head. It can do this because its neck is very flexible, so much so that its head can be turned 180 degrees on either side. An owl can look directly behind itself without moving its body. You try it!

Daytime birds not only display very bright plumage, they also see a greater range of colors than humans, including ultraviolet light. Their eyes also use another interesting method to detect different shades and colors. Each cone of a bird's eye contains a tiny oil droplet. The oil acts as a filter. It reacts to each color of light as it falls on the retina. These filters are especially sensitive to orange, yellow and red. This is why flowers pollinated by birds have these same colors! What amazing coordination! Who told the flowers about the birds' cones — how did they manage before the birds came along? The answer is simple and obvious. The phenomenal degree of sophistication — far more complex than any car — just like everything in the Creation, is the work of a master Designer and Coordinator Whose wisdom defies our finite mind.

"מַה גָּדְלוּ מַעֲשֶׂיךָ ה' כֻּלָּם בְּחָכְמָה עָשִׂיתָ"
How great are Your deeds, Hashem;
exceedingly profound are Your thoughts.

The Miraculous Mimic

I t sounds fine in theory. In practice, it is not so easy. First hear the theory. 'The most effective form of attack is the unexpected.' For example: You are walking down the street, and an unpleasant individual shouts abuse from the other side. In his mind he sees a vulnerable victim. He considers you a safe target, someone who will cringe under the verbal assault, and not retaliate. The last thing in the world he expects you to do is to react with defiance. Therefore, the most effective approach would be to stop, and in the most menacing manner you can muster, walk over in his direction. The theory continues that he will now be shocked, for this is not how you should have reacted. Shock produces fear, and fear will compel him to run away. The great risk in this particular example is that the obnoxious person might not run away. He might just stand his ground and return your bravado with belligerence. What will you do then? Alternatively, he might run away, around the nearest corner, where eight of his equally obnoxious compatriots are anxiously waiting for you to complete the *minyan.* This theory, therefore, like so many theories, is fine theoretically, but many centuries of experience have taught us that discretion is the better part of valor.

The problem of our wonderful family of Jacob is that we are perceived by the many members of Esau to be weak and vulnerable. Perhaps we are. We dress distinctively, physical prowess is not high on our agenda, and generally we are a mild, peaceful bunch of people. Would it not be beneficial, if, whenever we were threatened, we could suddenly change our exterior to resemble the toughest of the tough? Imagine. You are riding on a train, *yarmulke* perched on your head, immersed in your *sefer.* Suddenly the peace is shattered by raucous laughter from the end of the carriage. You have been spotted. The instigator of the laugh, emboldened by generous imbibing of alcohol throughout the journey, is heading (staggering) your way, with two cronies in tow. What was that theory again? Continue imagining that you could now press a little button on your belt. Instantly, you are six-foot-six inches tall. The muscles on your biceps swell until the seams of your jacket groan under the strain. Your shoulders grow to resemble an American football player, your face adopts the features of the world heavyweight boxing champion, with fists to match. You might glower in the direction of the three inebriates, and nonchalantly ask, "You want something, sonny?" With enormous pleasure, you see them gulp, grow pale, call for their mothers, do an about-face, and flee for their lives. With an indifferent shrug, you return to your seat, reset the button on your belt, shrink back to normal, and continue learning. Impossible?

For you, perhaps, but not for all living things. There are many animals which have been created with amazing talents for deceiving potential predators. Here there is no theory, it is all facts. You think that eyes are for seeing? Not always. Butterflies, for example, are usually so brightly colored that they appear to be offering themselves up as a delicious snack for every animal that feels like pecking. Apart from being brilliantly colored, many butterflies are also slow moving and generally quite defenseless — or are they? There is a large butterfly, the caligo butterfly, that lives in the rain forests of South America. It has two huge eyespots underneath each wing, which are normally kept out of sight. If attacked, it rolls over on the twig on which it is resting, and displays a scary face. You have to see it to believe it, but staring directly at you is an exact replica of an owl's two enormous eyes, large black circles surrounded by yellow, precisely resembling the owl's staring pupils. Not only that, the seam of the wings which passes between the two 'eyes' is raised, giving the appearance of the owl's horny beak. The big, round, frightening eyespots are the butterfly's secret weapon. Not for nothing is it also called 'the owl butterfly.' (Perhaps this illustration, more than anything, demonstrates Creation. Before you decide to resemble an owl, certain things are necessary. Most importantly, there has to be an owl to resemble. You have to know that an owl has a penetrating, chilling stare. You have to know that it has a hard, sharp beak, and that creatures are scared of that beak. It would be pointless going to a great deal of effort to resemble a sparrow, only to find that sparrows are everyone's favorite meal. And then, you have to survive without your defense mechanism long enough to allow your defense mechanism to develop. How are you going to do that? And if in any case you are managing to survive without looking like an owl in your spare time, why go to the bother of the Purim *Shpiel*? The clear conclusion must be that neither the owl butterfly as a whole, nor any particle thereof, has any knowledge of owls and their appearance, nor any ability to alter their own design. Their unique features are uniquely designed, by a unique Designer who has a master plan of the whole Creation.)

Press a little button on your belt.
Suddenly you are a cross between an American football player and Superman!

How well do you know your rhymes? Ever heard of this one? 'Red and black, friend of Jack. Red and yellow, kill a fellow.' It refers to two types of snakes. One is a coral snake; the other is a milk snake. The coral snake alerts possible mammal predators of its poisonous nature by the colorful bands that run along its length (red, yellow and black). The milk snake is clever. Why go to all the bother and expense (besides the inconvenience of extra weight, extra fuel, repairs and regular servicing) of carrying poisonous equipment, why not just resemble the coral snake? So that is exactly what it does. By clothing itself in almost the same pattern (red, black and yellow) and so closely resembling its venomous friend, and banking on the fact that most mammals don't learn nursery rhymes, the milk snake escapes attack even though it is absolutely harmless. Now why haven't all snakes thought of that — and for that matter, why didn't the coral snake think of it? It could have resembled a boa constrictor, or perhaps a roaring lion, or better still, an American bomber complete with stars and strips on its wings — that would give predators something to think about! Such questions, however, are futile. No international congress of snakes ever met to decide who is going to become deadly, and who will survive by resembling them. There is a Designer. There is a Creator.

The milk snake is not the only creature which has been designed to mimic its close relative. As we have seen, butterflies do it too. Birds know which butterflies are poisonous, and leave them alone. There are two such species, the poisonous friar butterfly, and the poisonous African monarch butterfly, which are copied almost exactly by two completely edible butterflies who live to flutter by another day because of their mimicking capabilities. The amazing thing is that it is only the female butterflies that mimic their poisonous relations, not the males. The males remain completely unprotected. If defense mechanisms were the result of the choice of animals themselves, there would be no logical reason why the males should not defend themselves. Do they not also want a long life? Why were they such *batlanim?* If, however, defense mechanisms are not the result of the creatures themselves, then it makes perfect sense that the Designer endowed some of them with a particular faculty, and others, for reasons known to Him, not. Ever wonder why you don't have wings? Same reason.

Most people, and creatures too, have eyes on their face. Could you imagine a creature which has eyes on the area normally reserved for sitting? In fact no animal has eyes on its rump, but the South American false-eyed frog has two large eyespots placed firmly on its hind-quarters. When the frog is threatened, it puffs itself up and faces its attacker back to front. The predator suddenly finds that its intended dinner has become a fierce face with two huge staring eyes. The predator does an abrupt about-face and runs for its life. Now here is a suggestion for you and me. We don't like being molested, so why don't we agree to grow a row of shark's teeth along our arm? The next time some unwelcome company tries to cause trouble, just roll up your sleeve and show them the rows of razor-sharp teeth glistening and damp in the sunlight — and see how they run. *Nu*, why not? If the South American false-eyed frogs can do it, why can't the false-shark-toothed humans? By now you can answer the question yourself.

The list is endless. There is a beautiful fish called a golden long-nosed butterfly fish, which has a large eye near its tail. Marvelous for reversing, you would say. The interesting feature of this eye is that it is completely artificial. It is not real and cannot see. Its purpose is to lure attackers away from its head. Not only that, it also hides its real eyes within a dark vertical stripe, rendering them virtually invisible. This fish spends much of its time paddling backwards to give the impression that its fake eye is at the front of its body. Attackers usually obtain only a mouthful of water, or at best a piece of tail, as the fish darts away in the 'wrong' direction. Now there's an idea for you. If you are worried about being mugged, grow another head (a false one, complete with eyes, nose and a mouth, perhaps with a moustache and glasses too) at the end of your left foot, and when confronted by danger wave your false head at the adversary. If a butterfly fish (long-nosed) can do it, why can't you? Who is more intelligent, a fish or you? The answer is that neither the fish nor we can change our design. The Designer is greater and wiser than both of us. The more we look into works of Creation, the more wisdom we see — we only have to look!

The Windshield Wiper

You just have to admit it. There are some people in the world who are clever. Not so much that they are highly intelligent — perhaps they are that, too — but clever in a practical way. You know the type of thing. Once upon a time, milk arrived at your doorstep in glass bottles. It was simple enough to press your thumb through the aluminum bottle top, and the milk was yours. Along came advancement, and with it, waxed-cardboard containers. Some people are clever. They read the instructions, pull back the flap and tear sharply, and in three seconds the job is completed, with not a drop spilled.

Other people are not so gifted. They can also read instructions, but what they experience is half an hour's struggle with the carton which resembles an all-out wrestling match, after which half the contents of the precious liquid lies on the kitchen table, and the remainder is divided equally between the bruised and battered carton and their splattered pants.

Take cat's-eyes. For 30 years drivers drove their vehicles at night along unlit roads. Their speed was restricted by the inability to see where the road was going. For 30 years no one could think of a method of alleviating the problem. Until one bright day, or rather one dark night, a clever man had a brainstorm. Was his name Herbert von Katz, as many people think? No, he was Mr. P. Shaw, a clever Englishman. In 1934, Mr. Shaw patented glass prisms, which were set down the middle of roads. They reflect car lights at night, thus guiding the drivers and making driving immeasurably safer. Simple and clever. Now think of grass. If you are blessed with a large lawn, how do you cut it and trim it? Nail scissors, perhaps, or do you prefer their big brother, the two-handed garden shears? Either way, it is laborious, back-breaking and inefficient; and yet for hundreds of years there was no alternative method. Not until the year 1805, when another clever Englishman (as you can see, England is famous for its clever people), Mr. Thomas Plucknett, designed the first lawn mower. It was simple enough — a circular blade moved by two wheels. The principle has not changed since then, but you had to be clever to think of it.

The gamut of inventions is great. Whether it is thermos flasks or Terylene, spectroscopes or sputniks, thousands of inspired ideas by clever people of all nationalities have enhanced and improved our lives, making life so much more convenient than it was in the past. (Just think of the difference between our age and only 100 years ago in the field of communication, travel, and washing shirts!) You have to be clever to invent. You do not have to be too clever to realize that an intelligent invention is the result of intelligence. Left to itself, the road (itself a conglomeration of many inventions) would not grow cat's-eyes, nor would garden shears develop wheels. Intelligence comes from intelligence. In the case of inventions, that intelligence is man.

And man himself? Does he have any clever inventions incorporated into his six-foot frame? Indeed he does. When you were little, or perhaps even now, no doubt well-meaning friends would tell you how closely you resembled your Uncle Chaim, or Aunt Faigie (depending on which side of the family they supported). "It's the eyes," they would gush, with doting enthusiasm. "Those blue eyes are definitely Fishberg eyes" (or Bernstein, or Goldman, as the case may be . . .). When people comment on the color of eyes, it is to the iris that they refer. Look at someone's eye, preferably with permission. In the center is a black hole, surrounded by a colored circle. The black hole is the pupil, and it leads to the inside of the eye. It is through that hole that light passes to produce an image on the retina, at the back of the eye. The pupil is surrounded by the iris, the only visible part of your eye to have color. What exactly is the iris, and what is its function? The iris consists of an opaque disc of tissue. It is in fact a continuation of a layer of the eye called the choroid, that runs from the back of the eye. What gives it its color? Nothing more glamorous than pigmentation, the same device that gives color to your hair. (Interestingly enough, people with blue eyes have no pigmentation whatsoever in their irises. The blue color is produced by a combination of the black inner surface of the iris, the blood capillaries, and the white outer layers.)

What is the function of the iris? Is it just to help identify you by its color? Much, much more. In front of every camera lens there is an aperture. Its function is to control the amount of light that enters the lens. The darker the scene, the wider the aperture needs to be, and conversely for a bright day. For years, the aperture had to be set manually. But clever people have been busy. Automatic cameras have been designed so that some of the light entering the lens is reflected downwards from a smaller mirror into the exposure meter. This calculates the amount of light available, and controls the length of time the shutter stays open, and the size of the aperture. In your iris there are two sets of muscles. These muscles are involuntary, which means that you cannot tell them what to do. They work automatically, and depending on the amount of light available, control the diameter of the pupil, and thus control the amount of light entering the eye. When you sit in a dark room, your pupil is large, to allow maximum light to enter. Go out suddenly into the sunshine, and for the first few seconds you will be dazzled. Allow your iris to extend, and restrict the light, and life will be bearable again. How does the iris measure the degree of light and darkness? Where is the exposure meter in the human body? How are the two irises in both eyes coordinated to ensure that they contract and expand together and at the same rate? Clever.

(You might like to know that the iris has been studied in great detail, and has been found to be a window to the general health of the person. The iris itself is composed of hundreds of tiny lines radiating out from the pupil. The science of iridology [study of the iris] has discovered that each line represents a different part of the body, so that a careful analysis of the iris can indicate the state of health throughout one's body. Amazing!)

Driving in winter has its hazards. One of the biggest is the state of the windshield. If the temperature is below freezing, you wake up in the morning to a frozen frosty windshield. Out come your scrapers, de-icers, rags, or in the absence of all these, your fingernails, to clear a path on the frozen landscape of the windows and side mirrors. As you sit hunched over the wheel, trying to squint out of six square inches of clear glass, the heater blasting out freezing air, you muse over the sheer delights of driving. If the temperature is above 32 degrees, there is the dirt and the spray thrown up from a mixture of slush and mud and brown rain. After five minutes on the highway, the windshield is filthy. How do you clean it? You can either lean out of the side window and wipe the window with the ubiquitous rag (not recommended even for pople with elatic arms), or else stop the car regularly and clean up. Now here is an opening for a clever invention. Did you say windshield washers in conjunction with windshield wipers? Who invented that brilliant idea? Must have been an Englishman!

But it works wonderfully. Fill the plastic bottle under the hood, press the little button and four fine sprays of water are pumped out of nozzles aimed at the windshield, achieving clarity that no window cleaner could have done better. Such a clever idea.

The problem is that in harsh temperatures, the nozzles can freeze up, and so can the water in the bottle. And it needs refilling. Shed some tears of joy for the magnificent invention that sits astride the two windshields in front of your face. Housed in the upper part of the orbit above the eyeball lies a factory that produces a combination of chemicals which is guaranteed to keep your eyes clear and clean under all conditions. The solution, popularly known as tears, is composed of the following ingredients: sodium chloride and sodium bicarbonate, to keep the exposed surfaces of the eye moist, and to wash away dust and other particulates; together with the enzyme lysozyme, a disinfectant, that has a destructive action on bacteria. The liquid is pumped through piping from the gland in the corner of the eye to several ducts under the upper eyelid. As the eyelid closes and opens (operated automatically once every four seconds by reflex muscular action) the wonder liquid is spread evenly over the surface of the eye. Do the tears not obscure the field of vision? Not at all. Tear fluid normally evaporates from the eye just as fast as it is secreted, but any excess is drained into the nasal passages through a specially designed lachrymal duct, which leads from the corner of the eye nearest the nose.

It's a marvelous invention really; the bottle refills itself, it never freezes, the nozzles remain unblocked in all temperatures. (Ever seen a frosted eye?) The gland which produces the tears is silent, which is unusual for a chemical factory, and the liquid, although a chemical mixture containing disinfectant, is completely odorless. What did we say before? — any clever invention demonstrates the presence of a clever inventor. Intelligence comes from intelligence. Welcome to the fascinating and inspiring study of the world we live in, in which intelligence shouts from every detail, pointing to the Greatest Intelligence of all.

The Juggler

Many things look simple until you try them. For example, what could be easier than diving into a swimming pool? You simply stand at the side of the pool with your toes curled over the edge, stretch your hands straight forward, tuck your chin to your chest, and with the tiniest of jumps project yourself forward in a graceful arch so that you enter the water with barely a ripple. Reality can be much different. Stretching the hands outwards is not too difficult, and curling the toes can be achieved with a minimum of practice.

It is the throwing oneself into the water headfirst that causes just the faintest hesitation. Perhaps it is the innate desire for self-preservation that creates the reluctance to hurl oneself into thin air. There they stand, cringing at the side of the pool, willing themselves to take the plunge, but unable to transpose strive into dive. Even among the brave souls who do take the plunge, their entry into the water more often resembles the submersion of a rhinoceros into its water hole, with the attendant sound and fury, than the grace of a dolphin. It is not as easy as it looks.

Neither is juggling (or playing the violin, tightrope walking, or flying a plane). What could be simpler? Take three balls of different colors, and place two of them in your right hand and one in your left. Hold one of the right-hand balls in your fingers. Throw the first ball in your right hand into the air. As it reaches its peak, throw the left-hand ball into the air. As the second ball reaches its peak, catch the first ball in your left hand, and throw the third ball from your right hand into the air. As the third ball reaches its peak, throw the first ball that is now in your left hand back into the air. Throw the second ball in your right hand up into the air as you catch the third ball, then catch the first ball in your right hand . . . are you following? Juggling three balls is really simple. (Try it!) If you want to attempt something difficult, try walking as you juggle, or juggle blindfolded, or cross your arms, bounce the ball off your knees, use four balls, or chairs, or — best of all — eggs! The truth is that for someone without training, juggling not with three balls, but with two, is a virtual impossibility. There appears to be a magnetic pull towards the floor! For someone to take several balls and keep them in a state of constant motion through the air, defying gravity for a considerable time, requires consummate skill together with mental and physical dexterity. The result, however, is both impressive and entertaining, and is certain to bring broad smiles to the faces of the *chassan* and *kallah* (unless you are juggling with eggs, and, as you juggle ever closer to the *chassan*, you slip, and . . !). If it is universally accepted that the art of juggling is indeed a skill,

Many things look simple, until you try them.

the question is whether this same skill can be observed in the created world.

The answer is both surprising and intriguing. Imagine that you have in front of you a piece of copper. With a very sharp cutting implement, you separate it into two halves. If it were possible to go on cutting it into smaller and smaller pieces, you would eventually arrive at a tiny particle called an atom. (Although an atom is invisible, it is possible to 'see' an atom. If you take the tip of a needle and magnify it about three million times through a powerful machine called a field-ion microscope, you will see tiny light spots. Each spot of light represents an atom.) An atom is the smallest particle that can have the chemical properties of a particular element. The word atom comes from the Greek 'atomos' which means 'indivisible.' Everything, whether solids, liquids, or gas, is composed of atoms. The world is composed of atoms, and every atom is a world! Each individual atom is a bit like a miniature solar system, with a nucleus in the middle and particles called electrons orbiting around outside it. All the atoms of a particular element are different from the atoms of other elements, and have different numbers of electrons. Because each atom has a different number of electrons orbiting it, each element has an atomic number. What is it that keeps the electrons orbiting the atom and prevents them flying off? (Imagine if that would happen — every atom would dissolve and that would be the end of all matter! Better not to think about it!)

The answer is truly remarkable. There is a perfect balance between two great forces. One force is the centrifugal force. This is the force that would like the electrons which are orbiting the nucleus to fly into space. You know yourself that when an Olympic hammer-thrower swings the hammer, which is held by a strong chain, around his head, it is only his strong grip that restrains the hammer in its orbit. As soon as the athlete releases his grip, the hammer flies free. The electrons would also like to fly free. What strong grip holds them in place? You have to know that the electrons have a negative electric charge, whereas the nucleus in the center of the atom contains protons, which have a positive electric charge. Since opposite charges attract each other, there is a force exerted by the nucleus (called a centripetal — or a form of gravitational — force) that keeps the electrons anchored to their orbit. The balance has to be exact, and it is. It is exact and precise to the extent that towards the center of the atom, where the nucleus exerts a more powerful attraction, the electrons have to orbit at a faster rate to maintain the counterbalance, whereas nearer the edge of the atom, where the attraction of the nucleus is weaker, the electrons actually orbit at a slower rate.

There are several observations to be made. Firstly, a

comparison to the juggler will show that the balls that demonstrate his skill must be kept in constant motion. He provides the thrust that compels them to rise into the air, until the more powerful gravitational pull draws them earthwards. Without his constant intervention, the balls would submit to the force of gravity and fall to the floor. Within the atom there is no one to intervene. Whichever power is stronger, either the centrifugal or the centripetal (the force pulling out or the force pulling in), will win. The very fact that matter and elements remain in a stable condition is evidence of the exact and precise balance that exists between the two forces. Nothing happens by itself. The atoms have not signed a contract compelling them to behave harmoniously. If the world would be accidental, why should one force not be stronger than the other? So there would be no world. So what? If everything is accidental, who says there has to be a world? The spinning balls of the juggler are evidence of great skill and expertise. The perfect balance that exists between the two opposing forces within every atom is powerful evidence of the most skillful of designs, that actually desires and directs the forces within the atom to be harmonious.

The second observation is no less amazing. As stated in the previous paragraph, the nucleus is composed of protons. These all have a positive electrical charge, and they are closely packed together. It is well known that opposite charges attract each other, whereas similar charges repel. Since all the dense mass of protons contained in the nucleus are positive, they should rip each other apart! Why do they not? Logically, there should be no such thing as an atom, for an atom without a nucleus is no atom! What holds the nucleus together? The answer is a mysterious 'strong force'; a mighty *koach* which compels the protons within the nucleus to defy their nature and remain together. Could there be a clearer example of design — a discernible power that forces particles to overcome their natural tendency, to give the world continuity?

At this stage, it would be interesting to point out that within the nucleus, there lies an enormous amount of energy. An atom is mighty small, but it can be split. When it splits, the great quantity of energy contained within the nucleus is released. Atoms can split naturally (as happens in the sun, where hydrogen is pressed together so tightly that its atoms combine, releasing great amounts of energy in the form of heat and light) or artificially. If they are split artificially, in a nuclear reactor or power station, then the energy can be trapped and utilized to provide light and power. As well as energy, the nucleii of some atoms also contains radiation. This radiation, although invisible, is highly dangerous, and is the basis for nuclear (i.e. the energy released from the nucleus of the atom) weapons.

And now for the third observation: When the projectiles of the juggler spin through the air, they do so because the juggler threw them there. They did not take off from the floor by themselves. Anything that moves must have had an initial thrust. The astronaut in space is only in space because a rocket projected him there. If electrons are spinning in orbit around the nucleus, something must have given them their initial thrust. Again we find clear evidence of a Prime Cause (Hashem *Yisbarach*) that gave all matter — from the tiniest electron spinning in perfect control around the nucleus, to the moon that encircles the earth, and all the planets in the universe — their initial velocity and subsequent orbit. Whether you look to the vastness of the Universe, or to the tiny world of the atom, the pattern of control and its great message of Intelligence is indeed universal.

Note: Italicized page numbers refer to illustrations.